MICHAEL FORSTER

ACT ONE

45 BIBLE DRAMAS

First published in 1996 by
KEVIN MAYHEW LTD
Rattlesden
Bury St Edmunds
Suffolk IP30 0SZ

0 1 2 3 4 5 6 7 8 9

ISBN 0 86209 849 1
Catalogue No 1500055

Cover illustration by Darren Regan
Edited by Stephen Haddelsey
Typesetting by Louise Hill
Printed in Great Britain

Foreword

Most, although not all, of these dramas are taken from my school assembly books *Wonderful World!* and *God's Wonderful People*, and here presented separately for use in the church context where those books may not be appropriate. All of them are based upon stories in *The Word for All Age Worship*.

As users of the earlier books will know, all the stories have been imaginatively rewritten while retaining and emphasising the original meaning. I hope that this not only makes them more enjoyable in themselves but also, in many cases, brings out other dimensions of the biblical texts. They are intended to be fun, but to make serious points. To this end, the dialogue is deliberately modern, and often colloquial, in order to make the characters as recognisably like real people as possible, rather than dim figures from the distant past, speaking in conventional religious language. It is intended also to make the dramas entertaining and to hold people's attention so that the essential points can be conveyed and remembered. It is of course open to individual readers to adapt the words to a style which best suits their own personalities or situations.

Each drama also includes some actions (indicated by a •) to involve the audience or congregation. It would be as well to give some thought to how these are to be included and led, before the day itself. The dramas may be enhanced, and individual talents recognised, through the use of dance, mime, simple costumes and sets.

I believe that 'all age worship' should be what its name suggests, which means that as far as possible it should be both accessible and satisfying for people of every age. So while I hope that these dramas will communicate well with quite young children, they also have other layers of meaning which may speak to older children and adults as well.

It has been a highly enjoyable task to produce this book; I hope it may be at least equally enjoyable to use, enabling people of all ages and at all stages of the Christian journey to learn and worship together.

MICHAEL FORSTER

Contents

A Boatful of Trouble

Based on Genesis 6:9-8:22

Narrator	A very long time ago, there was a man called Noah. He lived with his wife and three sons. They were all good people, and loved each other very much but the other people around them weren't very nice at all. One day, God spoke to Noah.
God	Noah, I want you build me a boat.
Noah	What, here? Whatever would I do with a boat when there's nowhere to sail it?
God	Just give me time, and there will be. I'm going to send a flood.
Noah	Now, why would you do a thing like that?
God	The world's in a mess, Noah, and I'm going to get rid of all the people and start again. Not you, of course. If everyone lived the way you do, there'd be no problem.
Noah	So you want me to build a boat for my family, is that it?
God	Er, no . . . not exactly. I want you to take some animals along.
Noah	How many?
God	Two . . .
Noah	Oh, that's all right – we can cope with two.
God	. . . of every kind that exists.
Noah	What? That'll be thousands.
God	Then you'd better make the boat good and big. And perhaps you should stop arguing and start building.

Narrator   So Noah and all his family got down to building the boat. What do you think they did?

- They *hammered*
- They *sawed*
- They *planed*

When they finished the boat, it was enormous. They got all the animals into it and shut the door just as the rain started. But Mrs. Noah wasn't happy.

Mrs. Noah   You didn't tell me when I married you that I was going to be cooped up on a boat with lots of animals.

Noah   I suppose you'd rather be out there, would you, in all that water?

Mrs. Noah   No, not really – but did you have to bring two of everything? I'm going to swat those flies before this is over, I can tell you.

Narrator   It was very hard – and the animals wouldn't behave themselves. The monkeys stole Noah's bananas; the hyenas kept everyone awake at night by laughing at silly jokes, and the elephants kept moving about and making the boat lop-sided. Everyone was very glad when the floods had gone and they could all get out of the boat again.

Noah   Well, I'm glad that's over!

Mrs. Noah   How d'you know it's over? God might decide to do it again, for all we know.

God   No I won't. I'm never going to do this again. And to show you I mean it, I'm giving you a rainbow.

Narrator   A beautiful rainbow appeared in the sky. And now, all this time later, when we see the rainbow it reminds us that God loves us and wants us to be happy.

Not a Lot of Brotherly Love

Based on Genesis 37:1-28

Narrator Joseph had eleven brothers. Can you imagine that!
I bet they had trouble remembering each other's names!
Anyway, I'm not going to tell you all of them, or you'll
be as confused as they probably were!

Now I'd like to tell you what a wonderful boy Joseph
was, and how his brothers loved him. I'd like to. But I
can't. The truth is that he was not a very nice person
at all, when he was young – although he improved as
he got older. As a boy, he was always telling tales about
his brothers – and his father believed him. Now his
father was Jacob, and he'd been no angel when he was
Joseph's age. So he should have known better than to
believe what Joseph was saying.

Anyway, one day, Reuben told Levi he'd had enough.

Reuben That brother of ours got me into trouble again today,
saying I'd neglected the sheep; and I hadn't.

Levi It wouldn't be so bad if he did any work himself,
but he doesn't. And now Dad's bought him a new coat.
It's got *long* sleeves! He can't work in that, can he?

Narrator That's true. Joseph couldn't do hard work wearing
fancy clothes, could he?

- He couldn't *milk the cows*
- He couldn't *clean the windows*
- He couldn't *paint the fences*

No wonder the brothers were angry. They were
going to have to do Joseph's share of the work!

Reuben That's nothing! What about all these dreams he's been
telling us about – dreaming that he's the greatest,
and we're all going to bow and scrape to him? I'm the
eldest, and I'll tell you this: I bow and scrape to nobody!

Narrator The brothers got together and decided to teach Joseph a lesson. One day, when they had taken the sheep a long way away looking for some grass, they jumped on Joseph and were going to kill him. Reuben was very worried.

Reuben Joseph might be a stuck-up little so-and-so, but he's still our brother. Don't kill him – just put him into one of these dried-up wells, and scare him.

Narrator Can you imagine how Joseph felt, being left in a deep hole in the ground? He wasn't tough and brave, like his brothers, because he'd been spoilt all his life. So he was really frightened and angry and he wouldn't stop shouting.

Joseph You come and get me out of here! You just wait until I tell Dad what you've done!

Levi I've had enough of this! The very next camel that comes along, he's on it. I don't care where it's going.

Narrator Very soon, they saw some Egyptian traders coming across the desert on camels. They ran and got Joseph out of the hole, and took him to meet them. They wanted thirty pounds for him but the traders beat them down to twenty. They handed Joseph over to the traders and watched as their camels disappeared over the horizon. Then they had another problem.

Reuben What are we going to tell Dad?

Levi I know. Let's say a wolf got him.

Narrator And do you know – that is just what they did. Jacob was terribly upset, because he thought he would never see his favourite son again. But of course, he was wrong. Joseph, as we know, was still alive, although very frightened. What no-one knew then was that he was going to have great adventures in Egypt. But we'll have to hear about that another time.

Joseph's Adventures

Based on Genesis 40-41

Narrator   This is a story about Joseph, who was taken to Egypt as a slave. He was soon in trouble again, and finished up in prison. Someone told lies about him. That's what he used to do about his brothers, and he learnt that it wasn't funny, when it happened to him! But then his adventures started. Anthony, the palace barman, was in prison as well. So Joseph tried to make polite conversation.

Joseph   What have you done to get put in here?

Anthony   Mind your own business!

Narrator   Joseph, kept quiet after that, as he had learnt not to upset people if he could help it. But next morning, Anthony was very thoughtful. He just sat in the corner of his cell, and . . .

- He *scratched* his head
- He *stroked* his chin
- He *shook* his head from side to side

Joseph couldn't contain his curiosity any longer.

Joseph   What's the matter? I hope you don't mind me asking!

Anthony   No – sorry about yesterday – I've had a funny dream. I was standing beside this grapevine with three branches. While I was there, grapes grew on the branches.

Joseph   What did you do?

Anthony   What I'm here to do – I squeezed the grapes, and made some wine for the king.

Joseph   Well, that's easy to understand. In your dream, each branch is like one day. So you'll be out of here and back in your job in three days.

Narrator   Anthony couldn't believe it when that came true! Of course, he could have told the king and perhaps got Joseph released, but he forgot. He was not at all grateful.

Two years later, the king had strange dreams, which no-one in the palace could explain. Then the barman remembered.

Anthony	I'm terribly sorry – I forgot to tell you – I had a dream, when I was in prison.
King	Don't come bothering me with your dreams! I'm too worried about my own.
Anthony	That's just it, Your Majesty. There was a prisoner called Joseph – foreign chap – and he told me what the dream meant.
Narrator	So Joseph was sent for.
King	It's like this: I dreamt that I was standing by the river, when seven fat cows came up from the water, and stood on the bank.
Anthony	Er . . . what kind of cows were they, Your Majesty – were they brown or black?
King	Don't interrupt, or you'll find yourself back in prison.
Anthony	Well! I only asked!
King	As I was saying, there were these seven fat cows. Then up came seven thin cows, and ate all the fat ones! Now what could that mean?
Joseph	That's easy! The cows are like years. There will be seven good years – plenty of food, and no-one will go hungry. But then there'll be seven bad years, without any rain, and in the end it will be just as if the seven good years had never happened.
King	That's terrible! What can we do?
Joseph	You need some help, Your Majesty. Put someone who's really wise and clever in charge of the country. You've got to save as much as you can in the good years, to see you through the bad.
King	Well I can't think of anyone wiser or cleverer than you. So it looks as though you've got the job.
Narrator	That was how Joseph became a very important person in Egypt. For the first seven years, he made sure that as much food as possible was saved. Then the bad years came. No food was growing anywhere, not in Egypt and not in the countries round about, either. But no-one starved in Egypt, because Joseph had done his job so well.

Baby in the Bulrushes

Based on Exodus 2:1-10

Narrator A very long time ago, in a place called Egypt, lived a really bad king. In his country were some people of another race, and he hated them. He made them work as slaves. Then he did something very evil, and decided to kill all their boy babies. So when a little girl called Miriam found she had a new baby brother she was very pleased, but also very frightened.

Miriam Mum, I've got an idea. Why don't we hide the baby in a basket? If we cover it in tar, it will float, and then we can hide it in the rushes at the side of the river.

Narrator So that's what they did. They put the little baby boy into the basket, and hid it in the bulrushes. Miriam decided to hide nearby and keep an eye on it, just in case. Imagine how horrified she was when a princess from the king's palace came along to swim in the river! The princess went into the water and began to swim, and then noticed the basket in the reeds. She opened it and saw the baby.

Princess Oh what a beautiful baby! But he's crying. He must be frightened, poor little thing!

Narrator So, what do you think the princess did?

- She *lifted* him up
- She *hugged* him
- She *rocked* him

Miriam was very worried. So she strolled along the river bank, humming a little tune to herself, until she accidentally-on-purpose bumped into the princess.

Miriam	Ooh! What a lovely baby! Is he yours?
Princess	No, I think he's a foreign baby. He's so beautiful, and I would love to keep him. So, since no-one knows whose he is, I'll take him back to the palace.
Miriam	Er, would you like me to try and find a nurse for him? After all, you wouldn't want to do *everything* yourself, Your Highness!
Princess	What a good idea. Go and find a woman from among the foreign slave people who can nurse him for me.
Narrator	Well, Miriam raced home as fast as she could and went bursting into her home, gasping for breath.
Mum	What on earth's the matter? It isn't the baby, is it?
Miriam	*(Breathlessly)* It's a princess . . . by the river . . . found the baby . . . wants a nurse!
Narrator	So Miriam and Mum hurried back to the river, and found the princess still there, holding the baby.
Miriam	Er . . . Your Highness, I've found a woman who can .act as a nurse for you.
Princess	That's fine. *(Turns to Mum)* You don't mind coming to live at the palace?
Mum	Not at all. Um . . . can I ask what you're going to call him?
Princess	I think I'll call him Moses.
Narrator	So the baby was taken to the palace, along with the 'nurse' who was really his mother, and the princess treated him just like one of the royal family.

Escaping Through the Sea

Based on Exodus 14

Narrator Our story is about Moses, the slave child who grew up in the royal palace in Egypt, He had always felt a little different. He never liked the way the wicked king hurt the foreign slaves, and one day, after a lot of arguments with the king, he led all the slaves out into the desert to find a new home. When they asked him where they were going, he seemed a bit vague about it.

Moses I'm not exactly sure where we're going, but God has told me it's a wonderful place. There's lots of food there, plenty of cream cakes and sweets. And most of all, you'll be free!

Narrator Among the people was a trouble-maker called Simon. He'd never really liked Moses, and he certainly didn't like the desert. He thought he would stir up a bit of bother.

Simon What have you brought us out here for? There's nothing but sand, heat and flies! We might have been slaves in Egypt, but at least we got fed!

Narrator Then everyone else started complaining, too. They'd already forgotten how dreadful life had been. Meanwhile, back in Egypt, the wicked king was getting complaints from *his* people, as well. They didn't like doing their own washing up, and they wanted their slaves back. So the king gave in and the Israelite people ended up with the Egyptian army on one side of them and a great big sea on the other.

Simon Well! Here's another fine mess you've got us into! We can't get across the water, and it's an awfully long way round.

Moses Don't worry! God will get us across. He won't let us down.

Narrator So there they were, at the edge of the sea, and somehow they had to get across. What do you think they did?

- They might have *swum* (but it was much too far)
- They might have *rowed* (but they hadn't any boats)
- They might have *flown* (but no-one had a flying licence)
- They might have *walked* (but it was too deep)

Well, it does look bad, doesn't it? But Moses knew what to do.

Moses I said God would help. All I have to do is reach out over the water, like this, and God will do the rest.

Narrator And he was right. God did an amazing thing! He pushed the sea back on either side and made a path right through the middle.

- So they didn't have to *swim*
- And they didn't have to *row*
- And they didn't have to *fly*
- They only had to *walk*

But Simon still wasn't convinced.

Simon That's an awful lot of water piled up at each side, and how do we know it won't come down on us?

Moses You don't – you've just got to trust God. But of course, you can always wait here and be captured.

Simon All right, I'll walk – but I'm not happy.

Narrator So they all went across. It was frightening, all right, with all that water piled up on either side. But eventually they got through, and God let the water close up again to stop the army from following. Now they were safe, and it was time to celebrate.

Moses Yes, but not for long. We've still got a long journey ahead of us.

The Walls Came Tumbling Down

Based on Joshua 6

Narrator Joshua had taken over as leader when Moses died. And he wasn't happy. Between his people and their new home stood a big city, called Jericho, and around Jericho were some very high walls. The people in the city had seen the Israelites coming, and a soldier called Seth was giving orders.

Seth Hurry up and get those gates shut or they'll be marching in here. That's better – now pile everything you can get up against them.

Narrator Before long, the gate was completely hidden behind an enormous pile of tables, benches, boxes, rocks and all kinds of other things. Someone had even brought a baby's cradle!

Seth There! That should keep them out! It'll take more than their little army to get through the gates now.

Narrator By this time Joshua was *really* fed up. And he thought it was time he told God so.

Joshua I wish Moses had never passed this job on to me! Being the leader of the Israelites is not easy! How are we ever going to break those gates down?

God Oh, don't worry about the gates; you're going to bring down the walls!

Joshua What?! Those walls must be ten feet thick!

God What's the matter? Haven't you ever heard of vibration? March the people round the city every day for a week, and at the end of it you'll be able to shake the walls down by shouting.

Narrator Well! Can you imagine the sight? Round and round they went, with soldiers in the front blowing their trumpets as loudly as they could. The enemy soldiers on top of the walls thought it was a great joke. Before long, they were selling tickets, and people were queuing up to buy them.

Seth Roll up! Roll up! Come and see the silly Israelites walking round the wall!

Narrator Every day more people came to watch. The Israelites didn't like the job much – people shouted insults at them and dropped rubbish from the walls – but Joshua made them carry on going round. Then at last, after a week, he gave the command.

Joshua All right, let them have it!

Narrator And what do you think they did?

- They *blew their trumpets*
- They *banged their drums*
- They *stamped their feet*
- They *shouted*

You never heard anything like it (even just now!) The air shook with the noise, and the ground shook with the stamping of feet, and the people watching thought it was great fun – until the walls began to shake as well. Then, gradually, cracks started to appear in the walls. The cracks got bigger, and the walls began to sway, and then there was a great CRRRRRASH! The walls had fallen down. Poor old Seth was amazed, and just stood there scratching his head.

Seth I can't believe it! All you did was shout and the walls just came tumbling down!

Joshua Well, there you are. It's amazing how much damage a bit of noise can do!

A Love Story

Based on the Book of Ruth

Narrator   This is the story of Ruth. Ruth was very happy with her husband, Chilion, and together they looked after his widowed mother, Naomi. Then something dreadful happened: Chilion died. In those days, there were not many well-paid jobs for women, so without a husband life would be hard. Naomi was concerned about Ruth.

Naomi   Ruth, you must go and find another husband – don't worry about me.

Ruth   But what will you do? How will you live?

Naomi   You mustn't worry about that; you're young and beautiful, and on your own you'll find a husband, but not if you have an old lady living with you.

Ruth   Whatever happens, we'll face it together. I'm not leaving you.

Naomi   Well, I hear they've had a good harvest in my home town. Let's go back there.

Narrator   So they set out for Naomi's home town, which was Bethlehem. (Have you heard of that before, somewhere?) When they arrived, Naomi's family were really glad to see her but sad that her son had died.

    Now, Naomi had a very rich relative in Bethlehem, called Boaz. And he was very kind, as well (which was lucky, because not all rich people are). Ruth got a job working in his fields. She went behind the people who picked the corn, and collected up anything they dropped. Naomi told Boaz all about Ruth's loyalty.

Naomi   I kept telling her to leave me and take care of herself, but all she would say was, 'Whatever comes, we'll face it together.'

Boaz   She's obviously a very special person; everyone's talking about how hard she works. I must find a way of repaying her. I know – I'll tell the workers to drop a little extra corn and let Ruth pick it up. And I'll make sure no-one gives her any trouble.

Narrator   While Ruth was working, Boaz went over to see her.

Boaz   What are you doing for lunch?

Ruth   Oh, don't worry about me. I'll just sit under the cedar tree to eat my bread and fruit.

Boaz   Well, I'd be very pleased if you'd come and have lunch with me.

Narrator   Ruth was really happy about that, and from then on she joined Boaz for lunch every day. They spent a lot of time together, and they soon realised that they were not 'just good friends', any more! Eventually, Boaz plucked up the courage to ask Ruth to marry him. Without hesitating she said, 'Yes!' because Boaz was a good, and kind man, and Ruth had come to love him very much indeed.

It was a wonderful wedding. Nearly everyone in Bethlehem came, and of course Naomi was given a special place among them. They sang and danced, and kept on drinking a toast.

- They *raised their glasses*
- They *shouted, 'To life!'*
- And then they *drank* every drop!

When it was all over, Ruth and Boaz settled down to begin their life together in his house. Before long, they had some more good news. Ruth was going to have a baby. Everyone was happy, and no-one more so than Ruth and Boaz. There again, perhaps there was one other person who was at least as happy as they were. Can you guess who that was?

Of course, it was Naomi. She was so happy she could hardly stand still – because she was going to be a grandma!

Biggest Isn't Always Best

Based on 1 Samuel 17

Narrator   Goliath had always been a bully. When he was a child, he used to take all the other children's toys. No-one tried to stop him because he was so big, and they were all afraid of him. It wasn't that he really wanted the toys – he just wanted to show how big and tough he was.

Goliath   Come on, then, who's going to fight me?

Narrator   He grew up from a nasty young bully into an even nastier old one. Then he joined the Philistine army and went to war against the Israelites. The Israelites didn't have anyone as big as Goliath, and everyone who tried to fight him got killed. Goliath used to enjoy showing off. Every morning, he went to the top of a hill, and shouted his challenge across to the Israelites.

Goliath   Send someone to fight me, if you can find anyone big enough. If he beats me, you will have won the war. Of course, if *I* win, *we'll* have won the war. Well, come on then, who's going to take me on?

Narrator   One morning, while Goliath was shouting insults, a shepherd boy called David came to the Israelites' camp. David was very small – about a metre and a half in his sandals. But Goliath made him mad!

David   Someone ought to teach that big bully a lesson! I'll fight Goliath for you, Your Majesty.

King Saul   Oh yes? And what are you going to do – hit him in the kneecaps? Ho, ho, ho!

David   You can laugh, but my mum says that biggest isn't always best. I'm a shepherd, and if God can help me chase lions away from the sheep, he can certainly help me with Goliath.

King Saul   Here, you'd better borrow my armour to protect you.

Narrator   Have you ever tried on a grown-up's clothes? Well, you can imagine how silly David looked and felt in the big man's armour. And when he tried to get the sword out and wave it, everyone threw themselves about and roared with laughter. David didn't think it was funny.

David   I'll make you sorry you laughed at me, and I don't need any silly bits of metal.

Narrator   I wonder what David would use to fight Goliath?

- He couldn't use a *gun*,
    because they hadn't been invented
- Could he have used a *bow and arrow?*
- Could he have used a *dagger?*
- Or might he have used a *sword?*

David didn't use any of those. He walked down to the stream, chose five smooth stones, and went to meet Goliath.

Goliath   Now what have we here? Are you the best that feeble lot could find? I'll feed you to the birds . . . I'll give you to the vultures for food . . . I'll . . .

David   Oh no you won't, because God's going to help me.

Narrator   At that, the giant lost his temper, and aimed his spear at David. Quick as a flash, David put a stone into his sling, swung it round a few times and let go. The stone flew through the air, and hit the giant, bang in the middle of his forehead. Goliath crashed to the ground, dead.

King Saul   I can't believe it! How can a little fellow like you beat a great big giant like him?

David   I told you – it's what my mum always says. Biggest isn't always best, you know.

A Right Royal Murder

Based on 2 Samuel 11

Narrator	King David could be a very bad man when he set his mind to it. Now you may be surprised at that, but even the best people can be bad at times. One day, in his palace, David noticed that he could see right in through the window of a nearby house where a woman was taking a bath.
David	I suppose peeping though people's windows is a bad thing to do – even if you are the king, or the government or whatever – but she is very beautiful. It can't do any harm to have a look, can it?
Narrator	But it could.
David	I know her! It's Uriah's wife, Bathsheba. What a shame she's married! There again, I'm the king – so anything I do must be right.
Narrator	But it wasn't.
David	I'll invite her for dinner. There's no harm in that
Narrator	But there was. Gradually, David and Bathsheba fell in love. Now, David knew that, even though he was the king, he couldn't marry Bathsheba. Then one day she had some news for him.
Bathsheba	I've got some news for you, and I think you'd better sit down before I tell you.
David	Don't be ridiculous, my little bath cube.
Narrator	When adults are in love they sometimes call each other silly names, but if children do it they tell you not to be childish. Had you noticed?
David	Just tell me the news.
Bathsheba	We're going to have a baby
Narrator	David sat down.
David	H – h – how did that happen?

Narrator   Bathsheba gave him a very funny look.

Bathsheba The real question is, what shall we do about it?

Narrator   David didn't know.

- He *scratched his head*
- and he *stroked his beard*
- and he *shook his head, sadly*

Narrator   Bathsheba left David alone to think. He knew that if Uriah found out, then, king or no king, he would be in trouble.

David   I've got it! Uriah's in the army. Now of course, since Uriah is a brave man and a good fighter it would be natural to put him in the most dangerous place, wouldn't it? And if he should then get killed in battle, well, that wouldn't be my fault would it? It's just one of the risks of war, isn't it? And then I could marry Bathsheba. I'm the king – it's perfectly all right for me to do that.

Narrator   But it wasn't. All the same, David sent a message to his general at the battlefield and marked it 'Top Secret'. In those days, that meant that nobody else would find out about it. When the next battle started, Uriah was put right at the front to make sure he got killed. Then David married Bathsheba.

David   No one will ever know the truth After all, people often get killed in battle. Of course, ordinary people couldn't do this kind of thing. If they did, I'd punish them. But I'm above the law.

Narrator   But he wasn't.

David   Of course, we did it all properly. We gave Uriah a proper military funeral, with a guard of honour, and said how brave he was and what a shame it was he'd been killed, and everybody cried a lot. So that made it all right.

Narrator   Oh, but it didn't. But David and Bathsheba were very happy together, and for a little while David thought he had got away with it.
But he hadn't.

A Right Royal Telling Off

Based on 2 Samuel 12:1-10

Narrator   I want to introduce you to Nathan. He was a prophet in Israel, and that could be a dangerous job. Prophets had to be very careful to say things in the best way. One day, God spoke to Nathan.

God   Have you heard what king David's done?

Nathan   I've heard some rumours.

God   Well, they're true. King David had an affair with Bathsheba – you know, Uriah's wife – and had Uriah killed so that he could marry her.

Nathan   Oh oh! Why do I get the feeling that I'm about to get landed with a nasty job?

God   Probably because you are. Go and tell King David that he's done wrong and he's going to suffer for it.

Nathan   Oh, sure! You know who'll get murdered then!

God   Use your loaf, Nathan! If you play your cards right, you can have the king on your side before he realises what you're talking about.

Nathan   Wait a minute – I think I might have cracked it.

Narrator   So Nathan went to see David

Nathan   I'm sorry to disturb you, Your Majesty. It's about a rich landowner and his poor neighbour. The rich land owner has lots of sheep and cattle, and his neighbour had just one pet lamb of his own. He loved it, and it was like a friend to him.

David   That's nice. Everyone should have a pet.

Nathan   This little lamb was the only joy the poor man had.

David   Why d'you say 'was'? Has something happened?

Nathan   Funny you should ask. It's that rich neighbour. He had a visitor, and wanted to give him something nice to eat. Now he'd got lots of animals, but he wasn't satisfied with that. So he stole his neighbour's little lamb, and left him with nothing at all.

David That's outrageous! Just because he's rich, that doesn't mean he can do as he likes. I'll make him pay for it! I'll make him wish he'd never been born!

Narrator David was getting more and more worked up. He strode about the room, waving his fist in the air.

David Tell me who he is! I'll deal with him!

Nathan It's you.

David Right! Call out the guard! Send for the executioner! People like this are –

Narrator David stopped in mid sentence.

- His *jaw dropped open*
- his *eyes stared*
- and then he *blinked a few times*

David W – w – What did you say?

Nathan I said it's you. You've got a palace full of beautiful women. Uriah had just one wife, and he loved her. but you wanted her, and just because you're the king you thought you could take her. You can't expect people to respect you when you behave like this. I'm afraid you're in for a very bad time.

David I deserve it. I'm really dreadfully sorry.

Narrator Soon after that, the baby of David and Bathsheba became ill. David stopped eating and spent every day praying, but after a few days the child died. David and Bathsheba tried to comfort one another

David We can't change the past – that's gone – but perhaps we can change the future. I'm going to be a better king, and that means being a better person.

Narrator David became a great king, and soon he and Bathsheba had another baby – a very special one – and they named him Solomon.

Having a Whale of a Time

Based on the Book of Jonah

Narrator   This is the story of Jonah. He was a fairly ordinary sort of chap, really – rather like people we know – but like many other people, then and now, there was something about him that really was not very nice. And we'll see what that was in a minute. Right now, God's about to spring a nasty surprise on Jonah.

God   Jonah, I've got a job for you.

Jonah   How exciting! What is it? D'you want me to rescue somebody from a dragon? Or is it a big famine somewhere that you need sorted out?

God   No, it's a lot simpler than that.

Jonah   Oh dear! How boring!

God   I want you to pop along to Nineveh and give them a warning.

Jonah   What sort of warning?

God   Just that if they don't start behaving themselves better they're going to be in trouble.

Narrator   Jonah wasn't very pleased. He thought the people in Nineveh didn't deserve to be saved, because they were what he called 'forriners'. That was Jonah's weakness – he just couldn't believe that God cared about people in other countries.

Jonah   I don't think I really want to go to Nineveh. Why should I save all those nasty foreign people? I know, I'll go on holiday to Spain instead.

Narrator   So Jonah got on a ship and settled down for a long cruise, but then the most horrible storm began. Everyone was frightened, even the really tough sailors! And Jonah was even more frightened because he knew why it had happened. After a little while, he did a very brave thing. He went to see the captain.

Jonah It's all my fault. I'm running away from God, and as long as I'm here, this storm's going to go on. I-I-I think you'd better th-th-throw me overboard.

Captain Good grief! What would your God do to us if we did a thing like that?

Narrator But the storm got even worse, and eventually they decided to do what Jonah said. So over the side he went, and as soon as Jonah hit the water, the storm stopped. All the sailors were very pleased – but what about Jonah? Of course, he tried to swim.

- He tried to do the *breaststroke*
- He tried to do the *crawl*
- He tried to do the *doggy paddle*

But he got nowhere. Still, God hadn't forgotten Jonah, and he sent a very big fish, which opened its mouth and swallowed Jonah whole – which was a good thing, really!

Jonah Well! Now what do I do? I can't think of a way out of here – or not one that I really fancy very much. I'd better wait and see what God's going to do next. And if he wants me to go and save those foreign people, then I suppose I'll have to go.

Narrator When three days had gone by, God got the fish to put Jonah back onto dry land – not far from Nineveh. This time, Jonah did what God had wanted. He walked right through the city, telling everyone to change before it was too late. And the amazing thing is that they listened to him. They stopped lying, and cheating, and fighting, and life became very good indeed. But Jonah wasn't happy.

Jonah I knew it! God's too soft. He's gone and forgiven all those nasty people, just because they changed. He should have given them what they deserved.

Narrator The strange thing was that the only person who ended up unhappy was Jonah himself. Wasn't that a shame!

Ride That Camel! Follow That Star!
Based on Matthew 2:1-12

Narrator   Melchior, Caspar and Balthazar were three wise men. They used to meet together often to talk about important things, and to look at the stars. They would sit around, very late at night (long after well-behaved children were asleep!) discussing whatever new star they had most recently seen. One evening, Melchior got very excited.

Melchior   Look over there! There's a great big star that I've never seen before. I wonder what it means.

Balthazar   I'll look it up. Let me see, 'Star – extra bright . . .' Hey, it says here that it means a special king has been born, and the star will lead us to him.

Melchior   Then what are we waiting for? Let's go and follow it.

Narrator   Everybody suddenly got very busy, packing the things they would need, and by the next night, when the star appeared again, they were ready to go.
How do you think they travelled?

- Would they *ride* on donkeys?
- Would they *drive* in a car?
- Would they *ride* on bicycles?

Of course, they would ride on camels, wouldn't they?

Balthazar   Come on everyone, let's get moving! The three of us will ride ahead and the servants follow behind with all the food and water and camping kit – and I hope you've remembered to pack the kettle.

Narrator   They travelled through the desert for many weeks, moving at night when they could see the star, and sleeping in their tents during the day. Eventually, they saw a big city ahead.

Melchior   Where are we?

Caspar	According to my reckoning that should be Jerusalem.
Balthazar	Good, that's a capital city. Let's find the palace.
Narrator	Now this was definitely a bad idea. The king in Jerusalem was the wicked king Herod – and he got a bit worried when he heard what the wise men wanted.
Herod	*(Aside, to audience)* I'm the king! There's not room for another one. I'd better find him and get rid of him.
Narrator	So Herod did a bit of checking up, and then went back to the wise men.
Herod	I think the king you're looking for is in Bethlehem. When you've found him, would you let me know, so that I can go to see him, as well?
Narrator	So off went the wise men, and Herod turned to his courtiers and started making plans.
Herod	Right! When those silly men come back and tell me where this so-called king is, I'll have him killed. King indeed!
Narrator	The wise men went to Bethlehem, and found Mary and Joseph with Jesus. They had some presents for the baby.

- *Gold*, for a king
- *Frankincense*, for God's special king
- *Myrrh*, for his suffering

Then they went to their tents to sleep. And next morning they got ready to leave for home.

Balthazar	We mustn't forget to stop and tell that nice King Herod where Jesus is.
Melchior	I don't think so. I've found out that 'nice King Herod' as you call him is bad news.
Caspar	I knew it! Shifty character! Don't trust him a millimetre! I vote we give him a miss.
Melchior	Good idea! Let's go home the pretty way.

The Man Nobody Wanted

Based on Matthew 8:1-4

Narrator This is a story about a man nobody wanted. We're going to call him Joe. He hadn't always been treated that way. Joe's family were farmers, and Joe used to enjoy life on the farm. Everybody liked him, and he was often invited to parties and dances. But that was before his illness.

Joe developed a very nasty skin disease. No-one's really sure exactly what it was, but it looked horrible! Everyone was afraid that if he came near them they would catch it from him. So they told him to go away. Grown-ups stopped their children playing with him and taught them to be afraid of him. Can you imagine what else they might have done if he came towards them?

- They might *put out their tongues*
- They might *shake their fists*
- They might *pull horrible faces*

Joe thought no-one loved him. He was terribly sad. Even his parents were afraid.

Joe's Dad I'm sorry Joe, but you can't stay here. We don't want the family going down with it, too, whatever it is. You'll have to go and live in the caves outside the town.

Joe's Mum Don't worry, we'll see you don't starve. We'll bring you food every day and leave it outside the cave.

Narrator So Joe had to leave home and live outside the town, right away from other people. His parents were terribly upset, but they couldn't think of anything else to do. They kept their word and took him food, but it wasn't enough. What Joe wanted more than anything else was to be hugged!

Then he heard about a man called Jesus, who could work miracles. So he went looking for Jesus, and what a surprise he got!

Joe Er, excuse me, Jesus . . .

Jesus Hello, how nice to see you. Is there something I can do for you?

Joe Aren't you afraid of me? Don't you want to call me names and send me away?

Jesus Now why on earth would I want to do that?

Joe Everyone else does, and you must admit I look pretty horrible!

Jesus But that's only on the outside.

Narrator Then Jesus did the most wonderful thing. He walked right up to Joe, looked him in the eyes, reached out and took hold of his hand!

Joe Wow! No-one's ever done that before – not since I got my skin disease.

Jesus Now that I've touched you other people will, too. They won't be afraid of you any more. Go into the town and people will be nice to you.

Narrator It was then that Joe realised that his skin disease had gone. His skin was as smooth and healthy as it had been when he was a child! Joe was very, very happy. Life was good again for Joe. He went back home, and his parents were overjoyed! He met up with his old friends again, children stopped being nasty to him, and he even got a job. But most of all, he felt loved, and wanted. And all because of a man called Jesus, who reached out and touched him when nobody else would.

The Barley and the Bindweed
Based on Matthew 13:24-30

Narrator Sally and Jake were both farmers, and they had been friends once, although they farmed in very different ways. Jake was greedy. He grew as much as he possibly could and sold it for the very highest possible price. Every single square inch of Jake's farm was always growing something. Sally used to leave a bit of her land wild to encourage butterflies and other wildlife.

Jake You'll never make any money out of butterflies.

Sally We've got to take care of the land, and not ask too much of it. Then it will take care of us.

Jake Sentimental nonsense! It's a matter of good stewardship. You've got to get all you can from the land.

Sally No, good stewardship is about caring for the land – and it'll give you more in the long run.

Jake Bah! Humbug! (Aside to audience) She'll soon go bankrupt, and I'll buy her fields at a knockdown price. Then I'll show her how a real farmer works the land!

Narrator But Sally's farm did better and better, while Jake's crops decreased. His foreman was worried.

Foreman 1 I can't understand it. The cabbages always used to do well in that field, but for the last year or two they've definitely been smaller.

Jake The crop's get smaller every year. Well, we'll just have to put more seed in to compensate.

Narrator Sally overheard the conversation.

Sally If you don't mind my saying so that'll just make it worse. You're taking all the goodness out of the land. Why not give it a rest for a year, and grow something different?

Narrator Jake did mind!

- He *shook his fist*
- and he *pulled a horrible face*
- and he *banged on the fence*

Jake   I do mind you saying so, actually. You go and mind your own business, Mrs. Knowitall!

Narrator   Jake was really jealous of Sally, and started to hatch a very nasty plan. Although he couldn't grow good food crops any more, Jake had plenty of weeds because they will grow anywhere, as any gardener will tell you. So he collected the seeds from them, and one night, while Sally was fast asleep in bed, he scattered the seeds among her crops. Very soon, Sally's foreman came running up to her, very upset.

Foreman 2   Quick! Come and look at the fields!

Narrator   Sally hurried off to see what all the fuss was about, and there – all mixed in among the crops were thousands of nasty looking weeds.

Foreman 2   I can't think what went wrong.

Sally   Don't worry, it's not your fault. This is sabotage, and I think I know who's done it.

Foreman 2   Well, I'd better get them out.

Sally   Oh no! Don't do that! You'll probably pull up some good plants as well. No, just let them grow together. My crops are good enough to stand a bit of competition from a few weeds. When we harvest it, that will be the time to separate them out.

Narrator   Sally was quite right: her crop stood up to the weeds very well, and at harvest time they had a grand sort out. Jake soon went out of business, because he'd destroyed the very land upon which it depended. Then Sally bought his farm at a bargain price and set about correcting the harm that Jake had done.

The Sale of the Century
Based on Matthew 13:45-46

Narrator   Abe was a very wealthy man. He had a big house, and fed on the best food money could buy. He was incredibly rich. How had he got rich? Well, he was a pearl trader. He used to make long journeys to visit the pearl fishers. They would sell him the pearls they found and he would take them to the markets and sell them to people like you and me. It was a lovely business, and Abe enjoyed it – but he wasn't really happy.

Abe   I'm sure there's a really beautiful pearl out there somewhere, and I want it.

Narrator   Then one day, it happened.

Josh   Hey, Guv. Want to see the pearl of your dreams?

Abe   I don't mind a joke, Josh, but it's been a really hard day.

Josh   No wind up, Guv– honest! Go on – won't hurt to look.

Abe   All right, but it'd better be good. Let's see it.

Josh   What, here? D'you want the whole world to know about it? Lord love me, Guv, I couldn't sleep safe in me bed if I thought anyone knew.

Narrator   Josh led Abe to a deserted cove, and furtively drew back some branches from the mouth of a cave.

Josh   No one knows about this, Guv. Get in, quick.

Narrator   Once inside, Josh lit a candle and rummaged under a pile of moss. Then, before Abe's amazed eyes, he brought out the most wonderful pearl Abe had ever seen. More than that, it was beyond anything he could ever have imagined. It was perfectly round, silky smooth, and seemed to turn the light of the candle into all the colours of the rainbow. Abe was entranced.

- He *held it up to the light*
- and *polished it on his sleeve*
- then *he held it up to the light again*

Abe It's, er, quite a nice one. How much d'you want for it.

Josh Come off it, Guv'nor. It's not 'quite nice' – it's absolutely stupendous. You've never seen anything like it before and I doubt you will again. Now if you want it it's yours but if you don't I can soon find another punter.

Abe Oh, no! Don't do that! How much d'you want for it?

Josh Well, I'm not a greedy man. All I want is a big house, some fine horses, and enough money to keep me in luxury the rest of my life. Shall we say a million?

Narrator Abe nearly died of heart failure. That would take everything he'd got. His beautiful house, his stables, his fine clothes and furniture – everything he'd worked for all his life would have to be sold to buy this one pearl.

Abe I don't know – that's an awful lot of money.

Josh It's an awful lot of pearl. Still, if you don't want it...

Abe Hold on – I never said that! O. K. I'll get the money.

Narrator Abe sold his house, with all its furniture and equipment, and went to live in a tent. He sold his horses and camels, and all the other things he had. Then he went to the bank and drew out all his money, and eventually he just managed to scrape together the million that Josh wanted.

Abe There you are – a million – just what you asked for.

Josh Tell me, Guv, how come you've sold everything you worked for just to buy this one pearl?

Abe Well, some things are worth much more than money, or comfort. You have to be prepared to give up the less important things if you want to have what's really valuable.

Come On, Cough Up!

Based on Matthew 18:21-34

Narrator Bart was a very rich man, who often helped out people who were poor. One day, he realised that one man – called Joel – owed him a million pounds. He didn't really mind, but he thought he should remind Joel.

Bart I just wonder whether you realise that you owe me a million pounds?

Joel I'm sorry, but one of my children is getting married, and my wife's ill. Please don't ask for it back yet.

Bart Look, why not just forget about it? Don't worry about paying me back, ever.

Joel Wow! Thank you ever so much. I'm really grateful.

Narrator Joel went off, walking on air!

Joel I must find some way of showing how grateful I am. I could buy him a present, if I had some money.

Narrator Just then Joel saw his neighbour, Nick. Nick owed Joel fifty pounds.

Joel Er, Nick, you know that fifty pounds you owe me – I'm afraid I need it back.

Nick I'm sorry, but I haven't got it. My father died, and I've got the funeral to pay for. I'll pay you as soon as I can.

Joel *(Grabbing hold of Nick)* Give me my money! Come on, cough up!

Nick All right, I'll have to borrow it.

Narrator Nick was really worried, and decided to ask Bart for help.

Bart Of course I'll lend you the money. Might I ask what it's for?

Narrator	Nick told Bart the whole story, not realising that Bart knew Joel!
Bart	What! Do you mean he attacked you over fifty pounds?
Narrator	Then Bart sent for Joel, who walked into the office without even knocking!
Joel	Wotcha, Bart!
Bart	*(Shouts)* Get out and knock! And don't come in until I tell you.
Narrator	Joel ran outside and closed the door. He was scared stiff!

- His *hands* were *trembling*
- His *teeth* were *chattering*
- His *hair* was *standing on end*

When he knocked, Bart recited a little rhyme to himself:

Bart	One, two, three, four, let him sweat a little more. Five, six, seven, eight, bet he's getting in a state! *(louder)* Come in – I'm waiting!
Bart	What's this I hear about you being unkind to Nick?
Joel	I only asked for what he owes me.
Bart	Asked him? Jolly near throttled him, from what I hear!
Joel	I only wanted to buy you a 'thank you' present.
Bart	What, by bullying my friends? And to think I let you off a million pounds! Well, I want it back by next week. And if you fail I've got a nice damp dungeon waiting for you with spiders and snakes for company.
Joel	I'll get it, I'll get it!
Narrator	Poor old Joel! If only he'd been as kind to Nick as Bart was to him, he'd never have got into all that trouble, would he?

Everyone Gets The Same

Based on Matthew 20:1-16

Narrator   Jack was a farmer who needed an extra worker to help with the harvest, and so he went into the market place.

Jack   What's your name?

Ben   My name's Ben and I'm looking for work for the day.

Jack   Right, are you any good at harvesting corn?

Ben   Oh, I've done a lot of that.

Jack   Then I'll pay you twenty pounds for the day.

Narrator   They went off together, and Ben started work. At about lunch time, Ben thought he'd better speak to Jack.

Ben   I won't be able to get all this done by myself today.

Narrator   So off Jack went, back to the market place.

Jack   What's your name?

Joe   I'm Joe. Nobody seems to have any work today, and I need the money to get myself a warm winter coat.

Jack   I'll pay you twenty pounds.

Narrator   So Joe started work. But they still needed more help and Jack went back to the market.

Dinah   No one seems to have any work today. I'll never get my garden fence mended at this rate.

Jack   What's your name?

Dinah   Dinah.

Jack   I'll give you twenty pounds for the rest of the day.

Narrator	So Dinah joined Ben and Joe, and at the end of the day Jack went out and called them over. He thanked Dinah for her help.

- He *shook her hand*
- and he *counted out her money*

Dinah	Thank you very much.
Narrator	Then Jack came over to Joe.

- He *shook his hand*
- and he *counted out his money*

Joe	Twenty pounds! But that Dinah woman got twenty pounds – and she'd only worked a couple of hours.
Ben	Joe's right. Dinah should get less than him, and he should get less than me, because I worked longest.
Jack	I don't know what you're so upset about. You're going to get what we agreed – twenty pounds.
Ben	But you've given her the same, and she doesn't deserve it.
Jack	I never said that she deserved it. I don't care what she deserves – I'm only interested in what she needs.
Joe	That's not fair!
Jack	No, it's generous – and that's quite different. If I was fair, Joe couldn't have his new coat and Dinah's garden fence would stay broken. Would that make you feel better, Ben?
Narrator	As it was, Joe got his coat, Dinah got her fence repaired, and after a while they all became good friends. Gradually, people stopped saying that Jack was 'fair' and started calling him 'generous', which was really much nicer, wasn't it?

Jesus Gets Angry

Based on Matthew 21:12-14

Narrator   Dan, the money changer was setting up his stall as usual in the temple, next to Joe, a dove merchant.

Dan   I like it here, Joe – better than being out in the rain.

Joe   Yes. Mind you, our stalls make it difficult for less able people to get in.

Dan   Who cares about them? They've never got any money.

Joe   That's true, and of course in here it's harder for the punters to compare our prices with the ordinary shops.

Dan   You're right. It's a pretty good swindle – and it's legal!

Joe   Just a minute, – what's all that noise outside?

Narrator   They listened carefully. It seemed to be some kind of celebration. They could just about make out words like 'Hosanna!' Then Jesus strode into the temple with his friends, and stood looking around.

Joe   He doesn't look very happy – he might cause trouble.

Dan   What! Him? He's a wimp! Talks about 'love' and 'forgiveness' all the time. He's a nobody – ignore him.

Narrator   So they did.

- Dan *counted his money*
- Joe *stroked one of his doves*
- while Jesus *looked from side to side*

Jesus   There are sick and disabled people outside who can't get in, and all the space is taken up by these money-grabbing swindlers!

Narrator   Suddenly, Jesus grabbed a piece of rope which one of the traders had left lying around, and knotted it to make a vicious looking whip. He went over to Joe.

Jesus   What do you people think you're doing?

Joe   Just a bit of honest trade, sir. Best prices in town.

Jesus   Best prices for you, you mean.

Narrator And then, without warning, Jesus grabbed Joe's stall and turned it over. The cages burst open and doves flew everywhere. Then Jesus went over to Dan.

Dan   Now look here, I've got a licence to trade here; I paid a high bribe – I mean tax – for it.

Narrator Jesus wasn't listening. He threw Dan's tray of money on the floor and overturned his table. After that, he drove the animals and all the traders out of the building. By the time the temple police arrived it was all over. Well, nothing changes, does it! Then a wonderful thing happened. Into the temple came a procession of people who had never been in there before. Some couldn't walk and had to be helped by friends; others were blind and had to be guided. They came over to where Jesus was standing, still a little out of breath, and a woman with a stick spoke to him.

Esther   Thank you. We haven't been able to get in before. The traders took up so much room, and all the people bustling about doing their shopping meant that only the really fit people could cope with it.

Jesus   I know, and it makes me angry! Now you're here why don't we do something about that leg of yours?

Esther   I've tried every doctor in the area, but it's incurable.

Narrator Jesus took hold of her hand, and suddenly the woman's leg grew strong again. Jesus moved on to the next person, and soon the temple was full of people laughing, singing and praising God while they jumped and ran around celebrating their new found health and strength. From then on, a lot of new people joined in things at the temple, who had never been able to get in before. They were very happy about it, although Dan and Joe and their friends weren't. But then, you can't please everybody, can you – so why try?

What Have You Done With My Money?

Based on Matthew 25:14-30

Narrator David was very rich. One day, when he was going away, he called three of his workers to a meeting.

David I want you to increase my business while I'm away. Let's start with you, Chloe. What are you good at?

Chloe I can grow things.

David Then why not open a garden centre? Here's ten thousand pounds to start you off.

Narrator Chloe went away, and David turned to Barney.

David What would you do with five thousand pounds?

Barney I could start a catering business.

David Good! Here's the money to start you off.

Narrator Barney left, and David turned to the third worker.

David Phil, here's two thousand pounds. What will you do?

Narrator Phil was scared to death.

Phil Er . . . I'll have to think about it.

David You make sure you do. Well, good-bye everybody.

Narrator Chloe bought some land and Barney bought a shop. Phil watched, thinking that they were going to waste all David's money. But he couldn't think what to do with his.

Phil Whatever I do will fail and I'll be in trouble. I know – I'll bury the money safely in the ground.

Narrator	So that's what he did:

- He *dug* a deep hole
- He *lowered* the money in
- He *patted* the earth over

	Meanwhile, signs were appearing all over the town, saying 'Come to Chloe's for Cucumbers' and 'Barney's Better Caterers'. (Don't confuse this with the other BBC, though, will you?) Business boomed and they had to make the High Street one way to prevent camel jams! Eventually David came back.
David	Well, how have you done while I've been away?
Chloe	Really well. I've made ten thousand pounds profit.
David	Well done, Chloe! I'll make you a partner in my business. Well, Barney?
Barney	I've made another five thousand pounds profit.
David	Wonderful! I'm making you a partner in my business, too. Now, Phil, what about you?
Phil	Er . . . um . . . ah . . . that is, well, you see . . .
David	Out with it! What have you done with my money?
Phil	N-n-nothing, sir. I kept it safe for you. Here it is.
David	Is that all you've done? I wouldn't have minded if you'd tried and failed. But not even to try at all – there's no excuse for that. Chloe, could you use another couple of thousand?
Chloe	You bet! I could open a refreshment room.
Barney	Yes, and I could do the catering.
Narrator	Poor old Phil! If only he'd realised that there's no shame in failing – only in not even trying!

The Man Who Came in Through the Roof

Based on Mark 2:1-12

Narrator   Barney was a wise and clever man who lived with his wife, Sarah. If anyone had a problem, Barney would listen very carefully and be really helpful. Then Barney became ill. He couldn't use his arms and legs any more. He had to spend all day lying on his bed.

Barney   Just because I'm paralysed, people treat me like a fool. Old Mrs. Wossname talks about me as if I wasn't there: *(mockingly)* 'Does *he* take sugar?' I ask you!

Sarah   They're very silly, but they mean well. Anyway, I've heard that Jesus is coming to town. Perhaps he can help.

Barney   Oh, Jesus is much too important to bother with people like me. How you put up with me I don't know.

Narrator   You can understand why Barney was frustrated.

- He couldn't *use a knife and fork*
- He couldn't *comb his own hair*
- But he could *watch*
- and he could *listen*
- and he could *talk*
- and he could *think*

And Sarah used to get really upset when he said he was a burden to her.

Sarah   Barney, I like looking after you. Now I won't hear any more arguments; I'm going to get you to Jesus if I have to carry you there myself!

Narrator   But Sarah didn't need to do that. She went and found four of Barney's friends and brought them back to the house. The four men picked up Barney's mattress, with him still on it, and carried him out of the door!

Barney   Hey, hang on a minute! I'm not dressed properly.

Sarah   Don't be silly! D'you think Jesus cares what you look like?

Narrator   Well, it was no good Barney protesting any more, because by now they were halfway down the street. But when they got to the house, there was such a crowd that they couldn't get in.

Sarah   We're not giving up now, are we, lads? Get up on the roof and get some slates off, and Barney can 'drop in' on Jesus.

Narrator   Inside the house, the people were startled when all of a sudden the tiles were pulled off the roof and a mattress started to come down. Jesus got up and went over to find Barney looking very embarrassed!

Barney   I'm ever so sorry about this. I'm afraid we have damaged your friend's roof. And I'm really sorry about the way I look, but . . .

Jesus   I do wish you'd stop feeling so guilty. Feel good about yourself – God loves you just as you are!

Narrator   Some of the people around were horrified! They thought only God could tell people not to feel guilty! 'Ooh,' they said, 'what a cheek!'

Jesus   *(Very impatiently)* Oh you are silly people! No wonder Barney's friends were so desperate! Look, Barney, why don't you get off that thing, roll it up and carry it back home with you?

Narrator   Barney was amazed to find strength in his arms and legs once more. He thanked Jesus, and his friends, and hugged and kissed Sarah. Then he walked home. People on the way actually talked to *him* instead of to Sarah and he'd soon made four appointments with people who wanted advice! Life was looking good again for Barney and Sarah!

Rain, Rain, Go Away

Based on Mark 4:35-41

Narrator   Jesus decided it was time to go home. It had been a long, hard day and he was tired. He knew his friends were tired, too; and they had quite a journey ahead of them to get across to the other side of Lake Galilee.

Jesus   Come on folks, let's go home!

Narrator   So they got into the boat and pushed off. Peter was a little uneasy. He knew that storms could be dangerous on that lake.

Peter   You go up to the front Andrew, and Thomas, you go to the back. And keep a special watch on those clouds just over the hills – I don't like the look of them!

Jesus   Well, I think I'll just go and lie down in the back of the boat and get a bit of sleep.

Peter   What do those clouds look like, Thomas?

Thomas   Not very good; they're black, and they're coming this way.

Peter   Right! Philip, you and James get that sail down, or the wind will turn us right over. Judas and John, make sure all the heavy boxes are secure; and everyone else, sit down, and hang on tight!

Narrator   He'd hardly got the words out before a sudden wind hit the boat, and blew it out towards the middle of the lake. It whipped up the waves until they were as high as houses, and the little boat was being tossed around on the top of the sea. Some of the waves came over the side, and the boat began to fill with water. Everyone was very frightened indeed. Everyone except Jesus, that is.

- The boat was swaying *from side to side*
- and rocking *backwards and forwards*
- and all the time, Jesus was *sleeping*!

Thomas was the first to notice.

Thomas Well! Look at that! We're working like mad to keep the boat afloat, and he's sleeping!

Peter Hey! Jesus! Wakey wakey! The boat's likely to sink any minute, and you're just lying there. Don't you care if we die?

Narrator Jesus got up and went to the front of the boat. There, he shouted to the wind and the sea.

Jesus Stop it! Be quiet!

Peter Well, a fat lot of good that will do! – Hey, why's it all gone quiet?

Narrator Would you believe it! The boat had stopped rocking. And it wasn't filling with water any more. Peter was so amazed that he just stood there, with his mouth open, looking for all the world like a fish!

Jesus Why are you all so afraid? Didn't you trust me?

Peter Wh-wh-what's going on?

Thomas Who is this man? Even the wind and the sea do as he tells them!

Jesus Well, that's that! Close your mouth, Peter, before you swallow a flying fish, and get us back home. Then we can all get some sleep.

Wake Up, Little Girl

Based on Mark 5:22-43

Narrator   Jairus was a very important man in the synagogue. He was married to Susie, and they had a lovely daughter called Hannah aged about twelve. One day, Hannah didn't seem very well.

Hannah   I was going out to play, but I think I'll just have a quiet day at home.

Susie   You never have quiet days at home. Are you ill?

Hannah   *(Angrily)* I'm all right! Why can't you leave me alone?

Narrator   And what do you think she did then?

- She *clenched her fists*
- She *screwed up her face*
- She *hit her palm with her fist*

And then she stamped off to her room, leaving Susie standing with her mouth open in amazement. A bit later, Jairus came home.

Susie   I'm terribly worried about Hannah. She's been really unwell all day. And this afternoon, she actually shouted at me.

Jairus   You're joking! Hannah never shouts at anybody.

Susie   I'm *not* joking. Hannah shouted at me, stamped her foot, and went off her room, and she hasn't come out since.

Narrator   Jairus knocked on the door of Hannah's room and went in. Straight away, he knew she was ill. So Susie rushed out and came back with the doctor, who hurried in to see Hannah.

Doctor   I'm afraid Hannah's very ill, and there's nothing I can do. What she needs is a miracle.

Susie	Of course! We know someone who can work miracles.
Jairus	Yes, Jesus does. But some people at the synagogue have been very unkind to him.
Susie	Jesus is too good a person to say 'no' just because of that.
Narrator	Jairus hunted everywhere, until he found Jesus. But just as he was explaining about Hannah, one of his neighbours arrived and said it was too late. Jesus didn't agree.
Jesus	What do you mean, 'Too late'? With God, it's *never* too late!
Narrator	When they got to the house, Jesus went over to Hannah's bed and took her hand.
Jesus	Get up, little girl.
Narrator	Then, to the amazement of Susie and Jairus, Hannah's eyes opened, and she sat up!
Hannah	Hello, who are you?
Jesus	My name's Jesus. What's yours?
Hannah	Hannah, and it's nice to meet you.
Narrator	Jairus and Susie rushed over to hug Hannah, who liked that very much but wasn't really sure what was going on.
Susie	Are you really all right?
Hannah	*(kindly)* Yes, Mother, of course I am. What on earth's the matter?
Susie	Jesus, we can't thank you enough!
Jesus	It was my pleasure. But you'd better give her something to eat.
Hannah	*(Looking very surprised)* Eat? No time for that! It's a beautiful day – can't I go out to play?

No Room

Based on Luke 2:1-7

Narrator   Simon and Susannah ran the local Bed and Breakfast, in Bethlehem. They were very caring people, and Simon certainly never meant to be unkind. But sometimes he did unkind things without meaning to – and this was one of them. So, not for the first time, he was getting a good telling off from Susannah.

Susannah   D'you mean to tell me that you turned that poor young couple away on a night like this – and her expecting a baby at any minute?

Simon   But we haven't any room, what else was I to do?

Susannah   Where there's a will, there's a room. I'm going to get that couple back here, and by the time I do, you'd better have thought of something.

Narrator   With that, Susannah went out into the night to look for the couple. Can you help her to look?

- She *looked to the left*
- She *looked to the right*
- She *turned her head from side to side*

And eventually she saw the couple. Their names were Mary and Joseph. They had been getting very worried, because it seemed as though Mary was about to have her baby any minute!

Susannah   Don't worry! I'm afraid that husband of mine is a bit silly sometimes, but he means well.

Mary   We don't want to be any trouble, but we really do need to find somewhere very soon.

Susannah   No trouble at all. You come with me. And if Simon hasn't thought of something by now, he'll be sorry!

Narrator   When they arrived, Simon was looking very pleased with himself

Simon   I still haven't got a room, but there's a shed out the back – not much in it, just a cow and a couple of goats, so it smells a bit. But there's plenty of straw, and anyway, it's all there is.

Mary   It will have to do. We're far too tired to go on looking.

Narrator   So Mary got comfortable on a pile of straw, but she didn't get a lot of sleep. Just as she and Joseph had expected, their baby son, Jesus, was born that night. They realised there was nowhere to put him, where he could sleep. Then Susannah had an idea.

Susannah   I know! We could put some clean straw in that feeding trough the animals are using.

Narrator   The animals weren't happy. They kept trying to get close to the manger. No-one was sure whether they were trying to see the baby or eat the straw!

Susannah   I think we'd better tie them up somewhere out of the way.

Narrator   So that's what they did. The stable didn't seem quite so bad as it had at first, but I think I'd rather have my own nice warm home, wouldn't you?

Never Mind the Sheep, Look for the Baby

Based on Luke 2:8-20

Narrator Jed and Enoch were shepherds. And Jed was rather a grumpy one – at least on this particular night.

Jed It's no good, we've got to get out of this business.

Enoch Oh yes? And what would you do instead?

Jed I don't know, but not this. All we do is sit out here all night, watching sheep, and we can't even go into the town for a drink, because the people all tell us to go away.

Enoch Well, you must admit that this isn't the cleanest job in the world.

Narrator Jed was about to make a rather rude reply when he noticed something strange. The sky was getting light.

Jed Wow! The night went quickly!

Enoch That's not the dawn. There's something funny going on.

Narrator What happened next made Jed wish he'd kept his big mouth shut about being bored! There, before his very eyes, stood an angel. Well, I say 'stood' – 'hovered' might be a better word, because he didn't seem to have his feet on the ground – he was just, sort of, *there*! Jed was terrified! What do you think he did?

- He *covered his eyes*, but he could still hear!
- He *covered his ears*, but then he could still see!
- So he *tried to do both at once*.
  But then he could see *and* hear!

Enoch Wh-wh-what d'you think we ought to do?

Jed (*Aside, to audience*) Well! Talk about a silly question! (*To Enoch*) Run like mad! What else!

Angel	Now don't be silly, I'm not going to hurt you. All I want to do is give you a message. Great news – about a special baby who's been born in Bethlehem. His name is Jesus, and he's going to save the world.
Jed	I'm sorry I said life was boring. Can you make it boring again, please? I promise I won't complain any more!
Angel	I'll tell you what; this will prove it to you. Go to Bethlehem, and look for a baby wrapped in swaddling clothes and lying in a cattle feeding trough.
Enoch	Which feeding trough?
Jed	Goodness me, there's thousands of them!
Enoch	That's what I mean.
Jed	Not feeding troughs, you fool – angels!
Narrator	And so there were! The sky was full of angels having a real whoopee of a time! Then, all of a sudden, they'd gone! Just like that! The field was dark again, just as it had been before.
Jed	What do you think we should do?
Enoch	Now who's asking silly questions! Go to Bethlehem.
Jed	We can't do that! Who'll look after the sheep?
Enoch	Never mind the sheep! We've got to look for the baby! After all your complaining about life being boring, then at a time like this you want to count sheep!
Narrator	So they set off for the town. They found Joseph and Mary with their little baby, Jesus. And the baby, just as the angel said, was wrapped in swaddling clothes, and lying in the hay in the feeding trough.
Enoch	Perhaps now you'll stop moaning about life being dull!
Jed	Me? When did you ever hear me complain about that?

Questions! Questions!
Based on Luke 2:41-end

Narrator	Joseph wasn't happy. He was tired, his head ached and his feet were sore.
Joseph	I don't know, Mary. Perhaps we ought to live a little nearer Jerusalem. At this rate we'll be ages getting home to Nazareth.
Mary	Oh, don't start that again! We like living in Nazareth, and it is only once a year we have to do it. Anyway, it's always worth the effort. You must admit it was a great celebration, and Jesus loved it.
Narrator	Jesus was twelve years old, and he'd certainly had a wonderful time, seeing all the sights of Jerusalem – such as the Temple and the Governor's Palace – and watching the big parades.
Joseph	Speaking of Jesus, where is he?
Mary	Oh, he's with Zebedee and Rachel. You remember, he spent most of his time with them in Jerusalem.
Joseph	Well, he's not with them now. Look, there they are – and there's no sign of Jesus.
Narrator	Mary and Joseph weren't really worried, but they thought they'd better check, so they hurried around all the other families who were walking with them, trying to find Jesus. Gradually they realised that he simply wasn't there.
Joseph	There's nothing for it, we'll have to go back to Jerusalem – and me with these feet.
Narrator	So they turned round and walked all the way back again to Jerusalem.
Joseph	Now where do we start looking? It's a big town, and it's full of visitors!

Narrator	For three days, Joseph and Mary scoured the city.
	• They *looked to the left*
	• they *looked to the right*
	• they *turned* and *looked behind them*
	But they couldn't find Jesus anywhere. The only place they hadn't tried was the temple.
Mary	He won't be in there. There are lots of things going on here that he'll find more exciting than religion.
Narrator	Even so, they thought they might as well try. So they made their way into the Temple and noticed a crowd in one of the courtyards gathered around a group of priests and teachers. In the middle of them was Jesus, listening very carefully and asking questions.
Mary	There you are! What d'you think you're doing, making your father and me so worried? Four days we've been searching for you – and him with his feet as well!
Jesus	Why worry – you should have known where I'd be.
Narrator	Joseph was about to say something very stern to Jesus for being cheeky to his mother, when one of the teachers spoke to Mary.
Teacher	He's your son, is he? Well, he's a bright lad, and he's going to go a long way.
Joseph	Yes, all the way back to Nazareth, and I hope his feet hurt as much as mine do.
Teacher	Never discourage him from asking questions. That's how bright children like him get even brighter.
Narrator	Mary and Joseph took Jesus home. They always remembered what the teachers had said, and encouraged Jesus to ask questions. And sure enough, he learned, and he became even wiser, and everyone said what a great man he was going to be.

What a Catch!
Based on Luke 5:1-11

Narrator	Simon and his brother Andrew, who were fishermen, had been fishing all night on Lake Galilee but caught nothing.
Andrew	It's your fault, Simon. You took us to the wrong part of the lake.
Simon	Rubbish! You didn't bait the nets properly.
Andrew	Don't blame me! I've always done well when you haven't been with me.
Narrator	Simon was getting angry. He was really a very kind man, but he sometimes said and did things without thinking first. But before he could answer Andrew noticed something strange.
Andrew	Look, there's a crowd gathering over there. Isn't that Jesus, the carpenter, talking to them?
Simon	That's right, he's mended our boat a few times. I wonder what he's doing here.
Narrator	Jesus had stopped working as a carpenter, and was going around telling people about God. When Simon and Andrew saw him, he was getting a bit worried, because the crowd were pushing to get close to him and, without meaning to, pushing him into the water!
Simon	Hey, Jesus! You'd better get into our boat unless you want your feet washed!
Narrator	Jesus got into the boat, which the brothers pushed out a little way from the bank. Then Jesus could speak to the crowd safely. Meanwhile, Andrew and Simon carried on tidying the boat, and forgot about their argument.
Jesus	Simon, why not go out a little bit further, now I've finished teaching, and see if you can catch anything?

Narrator	So they hoisted the sail and went out into deeper water.
Andrew	Where do you think we should try, Jesus?
Jesus	Oh, just a bit further on yet.
Simon	(*Aside, to audience*) Blooming cheek! I don't tell him how to make chairs! Why should he tell me where to fish?
Jesus	Sorry, Simon, I didn't quite catch that.
Simon	Oh! Er . . . I said it's very kind of you to show us where to fish, Jesus.
Jesus	Yes, of course . . . I think we should try here, Simon.
Narrator	So Simon and Andrew threw the net over the side and almost immediately the boat lurched over.
Simon	We've snagged the net on something.
Andrew	We can't have done, the water's too deep.
Narrator	They had caught so many fish that they couldn't haul the net into the boat. Can you help them?

- Come on, now: *Pull!*
- *Pull!*
- *Pull!*

Andrew	It's no good, we'll need more help, Simon. Isn't that James's boat over there?
Simon	Hey, James, over here – give us a hand!
Narrator	James came over, and they held the net between the two boats and got it to the shore.
James	Well, Simon, how did you get all those fish? My brother and I had just tried there and got nothing!
Simon	I don't know. Let's just say that as carpenters go, Jesus is a good fisherman.

The Soldier Who Believed in Jesus
Based on Luke 7:1-11

Narrator Marcus was an officer in the Roman army, and he had a servant called Septimus. Normally the Israelite people hated Romans, but no-one hated Marcus – as Septimus reminded him one day.

Septimus D'you know, sir, since you built them that synagogue, they love you even more than before.

Marcus I didn't do it for that. I just don't see why we have to be cruel to people whom we've beaten in war. They're good people and I like them.

Narrator One day, Septimus fell ill. The army doctor said he was dying. Marcus was very upset; he went to the market and bought him some figs to cheer him up. Jud, the fig merchant, thought it was strange for Marcus to do his own shopping.

Jud Is Septimus ill?

Marcus I'm afraid he's dying.

Jud I know who could help him. There's a man called Jesus who's always healing people. He's probably in the main square.

Marcus It's no good; he won't be able to go into my house, since I'm not a Jew.

Narrator But Jud was out of earshot. He'd gone running off without even getting anyone to watch his stall for him.

Marcus But from what I've heard, he doesn't need to come; all he has to do is say the word.

Narrator Marcus wrote a note, and got Nathan, a carpet seller, to take it to Jesus. Meanwhile, Jud had already found him. He went running up to Jesus, frantically trying to attract his attention.

- He *waved his arms in the air*
- He *snapped his fingers*
- He *pointed towards the market place*

Jud   Sir! Sir! Come quickly – someone's dying.

Jesus   Who's dying?

Jud   Septimus is. He's the servant of a Roman centurion.

Narrator Jesus set off straight away to find Marcus, with Jud leading the way. Before they had got very far, Nathan came running up and gave Jesus Marcus's note.

Jesus   It says: *Dear Jesus,*

Please don't come to my house. I'm a soldier, and not of your religion. But I know that if you just say the word, Septimus will be well again.

Yours sincerely, Marcus

Did you hear that? We call this man a pagan but he's got a lot more faith than most people of our own religion have. I've never heard anything like it before – not even in Israel! Jud, go and tell Marcus that Septimus is better.

Narrator Jud and Nathan went off like a couple of rockets. When they arrived, Marcus was about to go home.

Marcus   I've had a message from home: Septimus is better!

Jud   Wonderful! The healer said a really funny thing, though.

Marcus   What was that?

Jud   Well, he said that you had more faith than any of us.

Marcus   Really? What a strange thing to say! But do excuse me – I can't wait to get home and see Septimus again.

A Very Unhappy Person

Based on Luke 8:43-48

Narrator At one time, Anna was very happy. She had a husband, Abe, who loved her very much, and two sons, John and David, who thought that she was the best mum in the world. Everything looked good, until Abe noticed that Anna seemed to be ill. Now in those days you had to pay whenever you wanted to see a doctor.

Abe I'm worried about you, Anna. I think you should go and see the doctor – we can afford to pay.

Anna I think you're right – but I don't expect it will be anything serious.

Narrator So Anna went to see the doctor, and he examined her.

- He asked her to *put out her tongue (Ugh!)*
- He *checked her pulse*
- He asked her to *say 'Ah'*

Doctor Hmm . . . I'm not too sure about this. You'd better see a specialist.

Anna I don't mind that. How much will it be?

Doctor Well, that depends. The local one has a long waiting list, but I know someone in Jerusalem who could see you more quickly. The only trouble is, he costs more.

Anna I'll go to him – I don't want the illness to get worse while I'm waiting.

Narrator And that's what she did. But he couldn't help her either, and sent her to somebody else. And it all cost Abe and Anna an awful lot of money.

Abe I'm sorry, but we can't afford any more doctors. I don't know what we're going to do now.

Anna	I'll just have to accept it. It must be me – I must be a bad person, and God doesn't want me to get better.
Narrator	Now we know how silly that is – God doesn't want anybody to be ill. But Anna was very unhappy, until she heard that Jesus was in town. She could hardly believe her luck! Eagerly she went out to meet him. But then she became very nervous.
Anna	What if I really am a bad person, being punished? I'd better not trouble him. *(Pause)* I know! If he's so wonderful, perhaps I don't need to ask him. Perhaps I could just touch his clothes.
Narrator	So Anna crept up behind Jesus, and touched just the edge of his coat. It worked! She was better already! But then a really frightening thing happened. Jesus stopped. And he turned round. And he spoke.
Jesus	Who touched me?
Narrator	Now that sounded silly! People all around him were pushing and shoving, and he asked who touched him!
Jesus	Yes, and I want to know.
Anna	I touched you. I'm sorry if you're cross, but I'm ill and no-one can help me, and I thought that if I . . .
Jesus	Don't apologise! Do you feel better?
Anna	Oh, yes! Heaps and heaps better!
Jesus	Good. That's because you had faith. But you should never have been afraid; no matter how bad you think you are, you can always face me.
Narrator	Anna was over the moon! Touching Jesus' coat had cured her illness. But actually meeting him, had made her feel good about herself again. From that day onwards Anna always remembered a man called Jesus who had changed her life.

Neighbours

Based on Luke 10:30-35

Narrator   There was once a young man called Stephen, who lived in Jerusalem. One day, he was walking to Jericho when he got mugged. Poor Stephen was left lying on the road, bruised, battered, and with all his money gone. Then he heard someone coming. It was a priest.

Priest   What's happened to you?

Stephen   Stephen thought that was a silly question, and nearly said, 'I was out fishing and my boat sank,' but thought he'd better not be rude.

Stephen   I've been mugged. Can you help me?

Narrator   The priest didn't seem very eager.

- He *looked all around*
- and he *scratched his head*
- and he *shrugged his shoulders*

Priests   Terribly sorry but I'm on duty, so I mustn't get dirty. Don't worry, there'll be someone else along.

Narrator   The priest hurried away. Then a different kind of minister came along.

Minister   I say, have you had an accident?

Stephen   No, I've been mugged.

Minister   Oh dear! Are the robbers still around?

Narrator   And the minister scuttled off along the road, glancing nervously around him. Stephen was very worried now and really thought he might die. Then someone else approached.

Stephen   Oh, no! It's Tom, that Samaritan who sells second-hand donkeys. I don't trust him.

Narrator   In those days *everyone knew* that Samaritans hated Jews, and *everyone knew* that you couldn't trust a second-hand donkey salesman.

Tom   Dear me! You look in a bad way. Don't worry – I'll help you.

Stephen   But what about the robbers?

Tom   I expect they're long gone by now, and if they're not, they'd probably get me anyway.

Narrator   Tom rummaged around and found a bottle of wine.

Stephen   Hey! This is no time for social drinking.

Tom   I'm going to clean your wounds with it, not drink it! Now let's see what's the matter with you.

Narrator   Tom hadn't got a first aid kit, so he tore up his shirt to make bandages. Then Tom took Stephen to a hotel, and paid them to look after him there until he was well.

Narrator   Stephen could not believe what was happening.

Stephen   Tom, are you *really* a Samaritan?

Tom   Yes, I really am.

Stephen   Amazing! *(Pause)* And are you *really* a second-hand donkey salesman?

'Sunday Trading'

Based on Luke 13:10-17

Narrator Rachel had been ill for eighteen years! It was a strange illness that made it impossible for her to stand up straight. She had been to lots of doctors, but no one had helped, and it looked as though she would be bent double for the rest of her life. It was a great shame, because she had been very fit, going for long walks, swimming, and even taking part in the annual 'Donkey Derby'! Now, even simple things like hanging out the washing were impossible because she couldn't reach the line.

In those days, Saturday was rather like the Christian Sunday, but the law was much stricter – so strict that it sometimes got silly. This particular Saturday, Jesus was teaching in the synagogue. He saw Rachel come in, bent double, and he went to help.

Jesus What's the matter? Can't you stand up straight?

Rachel I haven't stood up straight for eighteen years! And even if I could, I'd keep my head down in this place.

Jesus Why?

Rachel Well, women don't have much of a place in the synagogues do we? Even if I could stand upright I'd be frightened to, in case someone noticed me!

Jesus That's silly! Everyone should be able to hold their head up in God's house.

Narrator Jesus took Rachel by the hand and lifted her up. It was amazing! Her back straightened, and she looked right into Jesus' eyes! Everyone was amazed, and some were pleased. But at least one person wasn't. Jerry, the synagogue leader was angry. He *said* he was cross with Jesus for 'working' on the Sabbath day, but some people thought that he just didn't like Jesus and was trying to catch him out.

Jerry	You've broken the law; you've worked on the rest day.
Jesus	Oh, really! I simply took her hand and helped her to stand up straight. Don't you want her to stand up straight in God's house?
Jerry	That's not the point. You're a healer – so healing is work, and you shouldn't work on a rest day.
Jesus	What if she was a farm animal and fell into a well? Would it be alright to pull her out?
Jerry	That's different. That's an emergency.
Jesus	So, farm animals are more important than women!
Narrator	Everyone laughed at that – except Jerry, who just got angrier, because people like that hate being laughed at! What do you think Jerry did?

- He *shook his fist*
- He *pulled horrible faces!*
- He *waved his Bible at Jesus*

But Jesus ignored him and went on speaking.

Jesus	You can feed and rescue animals on the rest day, so of course a woman who's put up with illness for eighteen years should be freed from it on the same day. She's just as important as you or anyone else, and don't you forget it!
Narrator	Jerry had no answer to that, and was very embarrassed. Everyone else was overjoyed. Someone even said that it was the best service she'd been to for a long time – and that just made Jerry jump up and down all the more! As for Rachel, she went home, singing and dancing, looking up at the beautiful sky, and stopping to play with every child she met on the way. From now on, life was going to be very different indeed!

Let's Have a Party!

Based on Luke 14:15-24

Narrator   Mike and Sarah decided to have a party. They invited their friends Joe and Elizabeth, and some others called Tim and Anna, as well as Eli, who was a newcomer. They all said they would come. So Mike and Sarah started getting the food ready.

Sarah   We'll have a fruit punch.

Mike   Yes, but be careful – not everyone's used to your punches!

Narrator   Eventually the food was ready, and the table was set out, and the 'Bethany Blues Band' was playing gently at one end of the room.

- One of them was *playing a trombone*
- One was *playing a piano*
- Another was *playing the drums*

Narrator   Mike and Sarah were really excited – but no-one came.

Sarah   I hope they haven't forgotten.

Mike   I'll go and check.

Narrator   First Mike went to see Joe and Elizabeth.

Elizabeth   I am really sorry but we've just bought a bit of land and we've got to weed it.

Mike   I wish you'd told us before.

Narrator   Then Mike went to find Tim and Anna.

Tim	I really am sorry but we've just bought this lovely new puppy, and we can't leave him all on his own, can we?
Narrator	When Mike got to Eli's house, no-one was in. Eli had got married and gone off on his honeymoon! Sarah felt let down and was angry.
Sarah	Well, someone's got to eat this food; it mustn't be wasted.
Mike	I know! Let's invite all the homeless people, all the ones nobody likes! They'll appreciate a party, even if our boring friends don't!
Narrator	Before long, the house was full of people having a wonderful time.
Sarah	Well! This is a bit different from our usual parties. No airs and graces – just folk who appreciate a good party.
Narrator	Just then, Joe and Elizabeth arrived.
Elizabeth	We felt *so sorry* for you that we put off the weeding and came. After all what are friends for?
Narrator	Before Mike could answer, they had swept into the dining room.
Elizabeth	*(horrified)* Good grief! What are all these revolting people doing here?
Sarah	Enjoying themselves, actually! Why don't you join them?
Elizabeth	*(snobbishly)* Not likely! Come on Joe, we're going home!
Narrator	The party continued well into the night. No-one wanted it to end. And I hear they're planning another – very soon! And inviting the same guests.

What A Silly Sheep!

Based on Luke 15:1-7

*Prepare placards in advance saying, 'This way to adventure';
'Juicy grass over here' etc.*

Sheep I never meant to cause trouble. I just wanted some excitement. Being a sheep isn't easy, you know – we spend most of our time following Joshua around (Joshua's our shepherd), looking for decent grass. I suppose I was always a bit of a rebel – always wandering off looking for excitement. My mum used to get so mad!

Placard holders Over here! – No, over here! – Come this way!
(As they call, the sheep starts towards each one)

Mum One day, you'll get into real trouble!

Sheep See what I mean? Parents! I just longed to be big enough to go off on my own without her stopping me.

Placard holders Over here! – No, over here! – Come this way!

Mum You'll learn the hard way – you just mark my words!

Sheep Yeah, yeah! Now where was I? Oh yes . . . One day I saw some juicy grass, just up the hill.

Placard holders Over here! – No, over here! – Come this way!

Sheep So off I went, and no one noticed. It was good stuff. And further on, it was even better. But I forgot to keep an eye on the others, and soon I was completely lost! I was very frightened (but don't tell my mum I said that, will you, because you know what she'd say . . .)

Mum I told you so! I don't like to say it, but . . .

Sheep   See what I mean? But I must admit that all this excitement was getting me down – and just walking along with the rest of the flock seemed like a wonderful idea! Then I had the fright of my life. Somehow, I'd wandered onto the side of a cliff and I was standing on a narrow ledge. Now I was *really* frightened!

- I couldn't *fly* up to the top, 'cos sheep can't *fly!*
- I couldn't *climb a rope*, even if I'd had one!
- I couldn't *hang glide*, 'cos I didn't have the gear!

Then, I heard something.
('Joshua' blows a whistle from the back of the hall)
That was Joshua's special whistle he used when we wandered off. If I hadn't been standing where I was, I'd have jumped for joy. As it was, I just gave out a little 'Baa' and I heard the whistle again – this time closer than before. So I gave him another 'Baa!' And that's how we went on – whistle . . . 'Baa' . . . whistle . . . 'Baa' *('Joshua' progresses gradually towards the front, still blowing the whistle when appropriate)* until he found me.

Joshua   You wait there.

Sheep   I ask you! As if I'd do anything else! He scrambled down to where I was and then he carried me up. I tell you, I closed my eyes and hung on. That was another thing my parents found embarrassing – a sheep that's scared of heights, I ask you! When we got to the top, Joshua put me down.

Joshua   Come on! You walked here, you can walk home. But don't worry, I'll be right with you all the way.

Sheep   He was, too. I'm more careful now. It's not so bad staying with the flock – in fact, we see some pretty exciting places. All I have to do is turn my head to the side – can't imagine why I didn't think of it before!

Whatever You've Done, I Love You!

Based on Luke 15:11-32

Narrator   Jonathan was a young man who lived with his father, Sam, and his older brother, Enoch. Enoch was very serious and worked hard, but Jonathan just liked having fun. One day, Jonathan asked Sam for a favour.

Jonathan   I don't want the farm, but I'd like my share of your money. Why not give it to me now, while I'm young enough to enjoy it?

Sam   I suppose you're a man now – you've got to make your own life. All right, here's your share. Use it well.

Jonathan   Oh I will!

Narrator   Jonathan knew of a country a long way away where everybody had fun. So he set off as fast as he could go. When he arrived, everyone wanted to know this rich young man! Each night he was at parties. And then he found the games-room. They didn't have slot machines in those days – they used people to take your money from you! Jonathan loved playing.

- He *dealt the cards*
- He *shook the dice*
- He *spun the wheel*

Jonathan never noticed how much he was losing, until one day he went to get some money from his bag and had a dreadful shock – there were only a couple of pounds left! He'd gone through his entire fortune! What should he do now?

Jonathan   I've got lots of friends who will help me.

Narrator	But when word got around that Jonathan was broke, his friends disappeared. He had to take a job as a pig-man. And he still couldn't afford food.
Jonathan	I'll end up eating the pigswill at this rate! Just a minute, though; my father pays his workers well. I wonder if he'd give me a job?
Narrator	Jonathan started the long journey home.
Jonathan	Now, what shall I say when I get there? 'I'm sorry Dad, I don't deserve to be your son any more. Can you give me a job – I'll work really hard this time, I promise.' Yes, that's about right.
Narrator	When Sam saw his son coming home, he ran and gave him a big hug. Jonathan never got the chance to say what he'd planned. His father called a servant.
Sam	Look who's here! Let's celebrate!
Narrator	Jonathan's brother Enoch was hopping mad!
Enoch	What are you doing? I've worked for you all these years for nothing, and now this lousy son of yours comes home and you throw a party!
Sam	He's your brother, you know, as well as my son. Won't you come and celebrate with us?
Enoch	Not on your life!
Narrator	There was a wonderful feast that night, but Enoch just stood outside, listening to the sounds. Deep down, Enoch wanted to go in, but he was jealous. So he sulked, and made himself even more unhappy. Wasn't that a shame?

Jesus and the Tax Man

Based on Luke 19:1-10

Narrator Zacchaeus was a small man – the kind who can easily get lost in a crowd. Some very cruel people, including some children, teased Zacchaeus dreadfully, calling him names like 'Titch' and 'Shorty'. Sometimes, when they thought they were being really funny, they'd call him 'Lofty' which was worse!
The way people spoke to Zacchaeus, he knew that they didn't like him one little bit.

Spectator Zacchaeus is a cheat.

Narrator You don't know that, do you? He might be, but there again he might not.

Spectator Well, he's a tax collector, and nobody likes them!

Narrator That's true. So people said that he was dishonest. They didn't realise how unhappy that made him.

Spectator Didn't care much, either.

Narrator One day Zacchaeus heard that Jesus was coming to his town. He'd never met him, but the word was that Jesus loved everybody.

Zacchaeus I wonder if he would even be nice to someone like me?

Spectator He'd be the first one if he did!

Narrator Zacchaeus washed, trimmed his beard, and went to look out for Jesus. The trouble was that there were lots of crowds, and little Zacchaeus couldn't see. So he climbed a tree to get a better view.

- The people *pointed* up at him
- They *shook their fists*
- They *made horrible faces!*

Spectator   Look at Zacchaeus, up a tree – now that's where he ought to live! Hey, Lofty – Have a banana?

Narrator   When Jesus saw Zacchaeus, he was kinder to him.

Jesus   What are you doing there, Zacchaeus?

Zacchaeus   Looking for you.

Jesus   Well, you won't find me up there! Get down and go home – I'm having dinner with you.

Zacchaeus   What, me? Why do you want to visit me?

Jesus   Well, not to pay my taxes – they're up to date! Look Zacchaeus, does there have to be a reason?

Zacchaeus   I suppose not.

Jesus   Good! Because my feet ache, my eyes hurt from the sun, and my stomach's shouting out for food. So come down and let's go and eat.

Narrator   People couldn't understand why Jesus was going to have dinner with Zacchaeus. Sharing food with someone usually meant that they were a special friend. And people who thought they were good didn't eat with people they thought were bad! So some of the super religious type were angry with Jesus.

Spectator   He shouldn't go in there; Zacchaeus is a bad man! I'm going along to watch and see what happens.

Narrator   Zacchaeus was as amazed as everyone else! So he stood up and made a speech.

Zacchaeus   I'm giving half of everything I have to charity, and if I've cheated anyone I'll give them back four times as much!

Spectator   Wow! That's a turn up – I wonder if he'll believe me if I pretend he's cheated me.

Narrator   From then on, Zacchaeus became a kinder, happier man, and everyone wanted to go and have dinner with him!

The Donkey's Day Out

Luke 19:29-40

Donkey   Well, there I was, munching on a mouthful of hay – because that's what donkeys do – when along came these two men and started to untie me from the wall. I suppose some donkeys would have been pleased but I wasn't very keen. Besides, my mother always told me not to go off with strangers. So I just dug my hooves in and refused to budge! You should have seen them trying to move me!

- They *pulled me from in front*
- They *pushed me from behind*
- They *got cross* and *waved their arms about*

And they used some words which well brought up religious people shouldn't even have known! Then, just as it was getting really interesting, my owner came out and spoilt it.

Owner   Hey! What do you think you're doing with my donkey?

Thomas   The master needs it.

Owner   All right. Now you stop mucking about, and go with these people!

Donkey   'Mucking about' indeed! I nearly said, 'You ain't seen nothing yet!' But I remembered some advice my mum gave me. 'Never talk to humans,' she'd said. 'It upsets them – they like to think they're the only ones who can do it.' So, off we went, and I had the time of my life!

When we got near Jerusalem, we met up with Jesus and his friends. Jesus sat on my back, and we set off into the town. What a racket! People were singing, dancing and spreading their clothes on the road for me to walk on.

I was getting a bit worried in case there was trouble. Some of the important leaders came over and gave Thomas a message for Jesus.

Thomas   Er, Jesus, some of the lawyers have asked if you can shut the people up.

Jesus   Shut them up? Impossible! There's so much joy around today that if the people didn't shout, the stones probably would!

Donkey   That told them! Mind you, it was a bit scary. I thought for a minute that Jesus was actually going to try to take over, and revolutions aren't really my thing. But he just went to the temple and caused a bit of a scene, while I was tied up outside. It turned out that Jesus didn't like the traders selling things in the temple, and so he threw them out – jolly good thing too! Then Thomas and Andrew took me home. I didn't think much of their conversation!

Thomas   It's strange – why didn't he ride a horse, like a real king – instead of this scruffy donkey?

Donkey   I tell you, I nearly refused to go another step! 'Scruffy donkey,' indeed! But my mum always said, 'Never cut off your nose to spite your face,' so as we were going home, and I was tired, I pretended I hadn't heard.

Andrew   Jesus doesn't want to be the kind of king everyone's afraid of. He loves the people and he wants them to love him. So he didn't want anything impressive – just an ordinary mule.

Donkey   It got worse! 'Ordinary'! and 'Mule'! I bet I've got a better pedigree than either of those two fellows had! They will never know how close they came to being in real trouble. But we were nearly home, so I just kept on going.

     I liked Jesus – he seemed different. And he treated me well. Yes, I like Jesus. But his friends – oh dear! I'm afraid they've got an awful lot to learn!

A Stranger On The Road

Based on Luke 24:13-35

Narrator	Cleopas and Joanna lived in a village called Emmaus, about seven miles from Jerusalem. They had gone to Jerusalem for a big festival, and to see Jesus. But Jesus had been captured by some bad people, and had been killed.
Joanna	Let's go home! I don't like it here any more.
Cleopas	Neither do I; the place is full of terrible memories.
Narrator	So they set out to walk the seven miles home. It was beginning to get dark when a stranger caught up with them, and heard what Joanna was saying.
Joanna	I can't understand how it happened. Jesus had so many friends, you'd have thought they'd have stopped it.
Stranger	Stopped what? What's happened?
Cleopas	You must have been walking around with your eyes closed! Jesus was killed – just because some powerful people were jealous of him.
Stranger	Oh, that! If you'd been reading your Bible, you'd have expected it. People like Jesus always get on the wrong side of powerful people.
Joanna	We did hear a rumour that God had brought him back to life.
Cleopas	Yes, but that was just some silly women – we men knew it wasn't true!
Narrator	Cleopas and Joanna did not know that this stranger was Jesus himself! The 'silly women' had been right! He walked with them talking of how the Bible said that God's special helper was going to get himself into trouble. By the time they got home, they were feeling better.

Cleopas	It's a dreadful shame that Jesus was killed, but perhaps God's at work in all this somewhere.
Stranger	Oh, yes, I think he is. God doesn't like bad things happening, but sometimes he can do amazing things with them when they do!
Joanna	Well, this is our house. Boy, am I glad to be home! Here we can feel safe. Nothing exciting happens here.
Stranger	Really? I wouldn't bank on that, if I were you. Goodnight.
Cleopas	Just a minute. It's late. Please come and stay with us.
Stranger	Thank you.
Narrator	The stranger followed them in to the house. They soon had a warm fire going, and put some bread on the table. Then the stranger did a very odd thing. Instead of being waited on like a guest, *he served them!*

- He *picked up* the bread
- He *broke it* into pieces
- He *handed it round*

Joanna	Good heavens! It's Jesus!
Cleopas	So it is!
Narrator	They both went to hug Jesus. But he'd gone!
Cleopas	Come on! We've got to get back.
Narrator	They scurried back to Jerusalem to tell their story. Philip said they already knew Jesus was alive because Simon had told them so. Everyone was wonderfully happy, and kept on telling the stories to each other.
Cleopas	Just think: a few hours ago, Jerusalem was a terrible place, and now it's the best!
Joanna	Yes. That often seems to happen when Jesus is around.

A Wedding with no Wine

Based on John 2:1-11

Narrator   Jake and Sarah were a lovely couple who lived not far from Nazareth, where Jesus lived. They had been saving their money for a long time, because they were getting married. They'd invited lots of friends, including Jesus and his mother. When the big day came, all the neighbourhood turned out to see the couple pass on their way to the wedding, and quite a lot of them actually went to the ceremony. Jake and Sarah promised to love each other for the rest of their lives, and everybody cheered. Then they went to the reception. Of course, the usual speeches were made, and the usual toast was drunk.

- They *raised their glasses*
- They *shouted 'To life!'*
- They *drank their wine*

Narrator   The caterer was getting worried.

Caterer   They're drinking a lot more than I expected and I think the wine's going to run out. If that happens, I'll never be asked to do another wedding within a hundred miles of here!

Narrator   Mary knew that Jesus wouldn't let people go thirsty. So she went over to speak to the caterer.

Mary   My son's over there – second from the end of the third table – he'll help.

Narrator   So the caterer went over to Jesus.

Caterer   Er, I'm afraid this is rather embarrassing, sir, but . . .

Jesus   I bet it is! You're out of wine, aren't you? You'll have to use those big jugs of water by the door.

Caterer   You can't use that – it's for washing in! It's not even drinking water – it's straight from the river!

Mary   Trust him and do whatever he says.

Narrator   So the caterer had the jars brought to Jesus. The jars were very heavy!

Caterer   Now what do we do?

Jesus   Pour some out, and let Jake taste it.

Narrator   So they poured out a glassful and took it to Jake.

Jake   Where's the caterer? Someone find me the caterer!

Caterer   Here I am, sir. I'm dreadfully sorry – I think one of the waiters must have made a mistake.

Jake   Mistake? I don't think so – this wine's terrific! Most caterers use the worst wine at the end, because they think the guests will be too drunk to notice. But you've saved the best!

Caterer   Oh! Er – well – um – all part of the service, sir!
(*Turns to Jesus*)
I don't know who you are, but you've saved me some embarrassment today, all right!

Jesus   I'm glad you're happy.

Caterer   It's strange – I know you're quite a religious person, but you still want everyone to be really happy.

Jesus   There's nothing strange in that. God wants everyone to be happy. He just doesn't want them to make other people unhappy, in the process. Now there's really nothing strange about that, is there?

Well, Well, Well!

Based on John 4:5-42

Narrator Jesus and his friends were out for a walk. Judas wasn't happy.

Judas I don't know why he's brought us this way; it's really a very rough area. The people can't be trusted.

Narrator The others were agreeing with Judas, but Jesus just kept on walking, until they came to a well.

Jesus This is a good place for a picnic. There are some shops not far away. Why don't you go and buy some food?'

Narrator Jesus' friends weren't too sure about that.

Judas We can't leave him here on his own. You know what Jesus is like – he'll talk to anybody – he tries to be friends with some very doubtful people.

Peter You mean, people like swindlers and thieves? Come on, Jesus can look after himself.

Narrator So the disciples went away, while Jesus sat down at the well. A woman called Becky came up with a cup in one hand and a bucket in the other to get some water.

Jesus I wonder if you could give me a drink from your cup?

Becky You're from the other side of the hill. People like you don't talk to people like me – we're different. You go to one kind of church and I go to another. If your friends knew you were talking to me – let alone asking me for a favour – they'd be very cross with you.

Jesus I could change your life, you know. Why don't you go and get your husband so that I can tell him, too?

Becky I haven't got a husband.

Jesus	But you've had quite a few, haven't you? Tell you what, go and get the man you're living with.
Becky	How on earth did you know about him?
Narrator	Before Jesus could reply, the disciples came trudging back with the food they had bought.
Matthew	There! I knew it. He's got talking to one of those dreadful women from the neighbourhood.
Narrator	How do you think Matthew showed his feelings?

- He *pointed his finger* at the woman
- He *shook his head sadly*
- He *turned his back* on her

Peter	Oh, don't be such a snob! None of us is perfect. Anyway, Jesus seems to have survived. She's just a woman like any other – people haven't got two heads around here, you know.
Becky	I'd better go, before your friends give you a hard time. I'll go and tell my neighbours about you!
Narrator	So off she went, and the first person she met was Judy who lived next door.
Becky	I've just met the most amazing man, from the other side of the hill.
Judy	From the other side of the hill? Surely you didn't talk to him – you can't trust those people, you know.
Becky	That's funny; that's what his friends were saying about us. But he's really worth meeting.
Narrator	When the neighbours met Jesus, they were amazed. They all finished up talking to each other, and forgot completely about which side of the hill everybody came from! Well, well, well!

The Biggest Picnic in History

Based on John 6:1-14

Narrator   Little Sam was well-known in his neighbourhood, with his uncombed curly hair, freckles and a big, permanent grin. He also loved listening to stories. It didn't really matter what they were about – he just enjoyed hearing them. So of course when he heard that Jesus was in the area, he wanted to go and listen. No-one could tell a story quite the way Jesus did – they were all about the kind of people and places everyone knew well; and the way he told them, you just couldn't help listening.
So Sam was really excited.

Sam   Mum! Mum! Jesus is here! Can I go and listen to him?

Mum   Well, I suppose I'll get no peace if I say 'no'! But you'd better take some food with you – once you start listening to that Jesus fellow, you're likely to be there all day!

Narrator   She was right. Once Sam got listening to a good story, he'd forget about everything – including going home for tea! Now Jesus wasn't actually planning on telling any stories that day; he really wanted to rest. So he took his disciples away into the hills, and didn't tell anybody where they were going. Unfortunately, it was about as hard to keep a secret, where Jesus lived as it is in - - - - - - - - - - - - - - *, so it wasn't long before just about everyone knew where Jesus was! And very soon, the 'quiet place' was full of people – about five thousand of them!

Jesus   Well, that's our peace and quiet done for! But these people must be hungry. Andrew, can we buy them any food?

Andrew   We can't afford all that!

Narrator   Sam thought he'd better try to help – so he went to see Andrew.

---

* The name of your town or village

Sam   Look, I've got five bread rolls, and a couple of fish.

Andrew   Hmm . . . Well, let's see what Jesus says.

Jesus   I think we can do something with this. Tell everyone to sit down, and we'll share out the food we have.

Andrew   It doesn't look very hopeful to me, but if you say so, Jesus, we'll give it a go. James, you start over there, and John go to that side.

Narrator So the people sat down, and shared the food.

- They *broke up the bread*
- They *shared it out*
- They *ate* as much as they needed

And can you guess what happened? Everyone had enough to eat! Not only that – when they picked up all the bits that had been dropped, they had another twelve baskets full of food. The crowd thought Jesus was just the person they'd been waiting for. They wanted to make him king – after all, he'd be a lot better than Herod! But Jesus didn't want that at all. Palaces, fancy clothes and servants bowing and scraping weren't his cup of tea!

Jesus   I think it's time to find that quiet place we were looking for – before things get out of hand.

Narrator As Jesus and his friends slipped away, Sam went home to Mum.

Mum   Well? What stories did Jesus tell today?

Sam   Oh, he told a few good ones, but what was really exciting was what Jesus *did*!

Narrator Don't you agree?

Living in Glass Houses

Based on John 8:3-11

Narrator   One day, Jesus and his friends heard a dreadful noise and saw a large crowd, dragging a frightened woman along. Jesus was horrified. But Matthew was a bit worried about getting involved.

Jesus   We've got to stop this. Look what they're doing to that poor woman.

Matthew   I'd be careful, if I were you. There may be a good reason for it.

Jesus   There's never a good reason to treat anyone like that! Whatever she's done, she's a human being.

Matthew   Well, I'd keep out of it. It's always best not to get involved.

Narrator   Jesus was going to say something very stern to Matthew, but by that time the crowd were really wound up!

- They were *rolling up their sleeves*
- They were *picking up stones*
- They were *taking aim*

So Jesus spoke to the mob leader – a nasty, vindictive character, called Josh.

Jesus   What on earth do you think you're doing?

Josh   We're going to throw stones at her until she's dead.

Matthew   You'd better keep out of this one, Jesus. They've all got stones in their hands, and I'm afraid some of them might get thrown at us.

Jesus	What? Let them stone this woman to death? I'm not going to stand by and let that happen.
Josh	I've had enough of this! Come on, let's get on with it.
Jesus	You'll have to get past me first! Why do you want to do this, anyway?
Josh	*(with an evil grin)* She's always breaking the law – so we're going to enforce it.
Jesus	But who do you think you are?
Josh	*(smugly)* An honest, respectable citizen.
Jesus	You mean you've never been caught! I'll tell you what, Josh: if there's anyone among you who has never done anything wrong – anything at all, no matter how tiny – they can throw the first stone.
Narrator	Well! You could have heard a pin drop! Josh knew that, whatever he said to other people, he wasn't really as good as all that. After a few moments, he let go of his stone and it clattered down the hill. Then someone else did the same, and soon the square was filled with the sound of rolling stones. What a row! Gradually people turned and walked away. Eventually, only Jesus, his friends and the woman were left.
Jesus	Now you've got the chance to start again. You can be different from now on!
Narrator	The woman was so relieved that she just ran home!
Jesus	You know, when it comes to throwing stones at others, people usually find that they're living in glass houses themselves!

I Can See!

Based on John 9:1-39

Narrator   Tim was very clever. But every day he sat in the streets begging. Tim had been born blind, which in those days meant he couldn't go to school, or get a job. The rest of him worked well – he could hear, smell, talk. It was just that he couldn't see. And because of that one thing, everyone thought he was useless. Poor Tim! One day Jesus and his friends walked past and Matthew asked Jesus a question.

Matthew   Why's he blind, Jesus? Did his parents do something dreadful, and God's punishing them, or is he the one who's being punished?

Jesus   You don't really think God would do that, do you?

Narrator   Then Jesus did something very strange. He made some mud from the dust on the ground, and smeared it on Tim's eyes. Tim wasn't impressed at first!

Tim   Hey! Leave me alone – GERROFF!

Jesus   Don't worry. My name is Jesus, and I want to help you to see. Now go and wash in the pond over there.

Tim   You bet I will – fancy doing a thing like that!

Narrator   When Tim got to the pool . . .

- He *washed his face*
- He *blinked* in amazement
- He *jumped* for joy

Tim   Hey, everybody, I can see!

Narrator	After a little while, some posh people heard the noise and came to see what it was all about.
Tim	I can see! I can see!
Paul	Don't be silly! You're blind – I've seen you begging.
Tim	Yes, Paul, but I can see now! Look, I can see a donkey over there, and there's a camel, and . . .
Paul	All right, calm down! How did this happen?
Tim	Well, it was the funniest thing. This man called Jesus put some mud on my eyes and told me to wash. I thought he was barmy, I don't mind telling you – but now I can see!
Paul	*(Aside, to audience)* That troublemaker Jesus again! If this goes on, people will think that Jesus is more important than I am.
	(To Tim) You're a liar. You just pretended to be blind to get easy money.
Tim	Don't be silly, Paul! I'd be better off working!
Paul	All right, I believe you. But this is the day of rest. So if Jesus healed you today he must be an evil man.
Tim	Evil? How can someone who helps people be evil?
Paul	Jesus can't have come from God, or we lawyers would have known about him. We don't know who he is.
Tim	Well, there's a funny thing! You clever lot can't see what's right in front of your noses – and to think, people used to say that I was blind!

Dead and Alive Again

Based on the Passion and Resurrection Narratives

Narrator   Not everyone liked Jesus. Some people liked to think they were important, and were afraid Jesus might get to be more important than they were. Others didn't like what Jesus said. So one day, some of these people (who thought they were good, but were really not nice at all) said horrible things about Jesus and had him killed. Jesus' enemies thought they'd won. What they didn't know, of course, was that they *hadn't* got rid of him, at all! Jesus was killed on the Friday. Then on the Sunday, Mary Magdalene and her friends had an idea.

Mary   I'm going to Jesus' grave. I want to put some flowers on it. Coming, Joanna?

Joanna   I'm not sure. Won't the people who killed Jesus be watching his grave, to find out who his friends are?

Mary   So what? They know about us, anyway.

Joanna   I suppose you're right, Mary – I'd like to go.

Narrator   So they went together but when they got there, they found that the grave was empty. They were very puzzled.

- They *scratched their heads*
- They *wrung their hands*
- They *peered all round*

Then they noticed a stranger waiting there.

Stranger   It's no good looking for Jesus here – he's alive again, so what would he be doing in a grave?

Narrator   Joanna was terrified! She didn't know what was going on, but she knew she didn't like it! So she ran off, but Mary Magdalene stayed. What was said hadn't sunk in, and she was still wondering what to do when she thought she saw the gardener. It was not really light yet, and she couldn't see clearly.

Mary   Excuse me, I've come to find Jesus' grave.

Jesus   Mary!

Narrator   It was Jesus! He *was* alive again! Mary went to grab him, but Jesus stopped her.

Jesus   Don't cling on to me! You can't just hang on to the past. We've got new things to do, now! Go and tell the others that I'm alive.

Mary   Shall I bring them back here?

Jesus   Oh no! I'm not going to hang around in this place for ever – I've got work to do.

Mary   So where will they find you?

Jesus   Where they always have – out in the world. Wherever people are, there they'll find me.

Narrator   So Mary ran back and told the disciples what Jesus had said.

Mary   He's alive, and no-one's ever going to be able to kill him again. He's going to be here forever, even when we can't see him, and he'll never leave us.

Narrator   And d'you know, she was quite right.

I'll Believe It When I See It

Based on John 20:24-29

Narrator   After Jesus had risen from the dead, Mary Magdalene ran and told his friends all about it. But none of the men believed it. Then, as they were arguing, Jesus was suddenly standing among them! They were terrified!

- They *covered their faces*
- They *peeped between their fingers*
- Then they *covered their faces again*

They thought it must be a ghost! Then he spoke to them.

Jesus   Don't worry, I'm not a ghost. Here, come and take hold of my hand, just to prove that I'm real.

Narrator   Very gingerly, Peter took Jesus' hand.

Peter   It's true! It really is him!

Narrator   Then everyone went wild! They all crowded round Jesus, asking questions.

Jesus   The important thing is that God has brought me back to life. Your job is to go and tell everybody that – not argue about how he did it!

Narrator   Then, all of a sudden, he was gone! His friends had never been too sure what Jesus was going to do next. But now he seemed to be able to come and go as he liked.

Peter   No-one's ever been able to pin Jesus down. He's not just alive, he's *free* as well!

Narrator   Just then, Thomas came in. He could tell that everybody was excited.

Thomas	What's going on?
Philip	Jesus has been here; he's alive.
Thomas	Pull the other one, Philip!
Narrator	Peter and Philip simply couldn't convince him.
Thomas	I'll tell you what: if I can see him, and touch him, I'll believe he's alive. But not until!
Philip	Why? Don't you trust your own friends?
Thomas	Not a lot! Remember when you told me the easy way to count sheep was to count the legs and divide by four?
Philip	And you actually tried it!
Thomas	Laugh if you like, but you're not catching me again.
Narrator	With that, Thomas went home. A week later Jesus appeared again, and this time Thomas was there, and he was overjoyed!
Thomas	It's true! My master – alive!
Jesus	You've seen me, and now you can believe. It's going to be harder for people who don't see me. You've got to go and help them.
Narrator	Some of the disciples used to tease Thomas after that, because he had doubted what they had told him. I expect he probably said that they had no room to talk – they didn't believe it, either, when the women first told them. They had to see before they believed, just like Thomas. And of course, he would have been quite right, wouldn't he?

Don't Just Sit There

Based on Acts 3:1-10

Narrator   Have your legs ever felt like jelly – perhaps because you were frightened? Well, Jamie's legs were always like that. The rest of his body was fine, and his brain was great – but his legs wouldn't work at all! Every day, Jamie's friends carried him to the temple in Jerusalem and sat him down by the 'Beautiful Gate', where he could beg. Jamie hated it! It was so embarrassing!

Jamie   I've got a first class brain, and I can use my hands, but you'd think I was completely useless, just because my legs won't work!

Narrator   What sort of things do you think Jamie could do?

- Perhaps he could *paint pictures*
- Maybe he could *play a trumpet*
- Or *use a hammer*

Narrator   But no-one thought of that! One afternoon, Peter and John were going to the temple. Jesus had gone back to heaven, but he'd said he'd always be with them although they couldn't see him.

John   We must tell everybody about Jesus, Peter.

Peter   The point is that Jesus has shown us what God is like. If people knew that God was like Jesus, they'd love him more and be less frightened of him.

John   Yes, I know, Peter, but how do we show them that?

Peter   We must let Jesus use our hands to help people.

John   Fine, but first, we've got to let him use our ears to listen. That man, for example – what's he saying?

Peter   Let's ask him, John. What do you want?

Jamie	*(Aside to audience)* They must be deaf! *(To Peter)* I need money.
Peter	I know you need money, but what do you *really want?*
Jamie	Oh, that's different! I want to be able to stand up on these silly legs. I want to be able to talk to people without their bending down to me as if I were a baby in a pram! I want to be able to walk into that temple on my own two legs – I want to run, and jump, and kick a ball like anyone else. I want . . .
John	Yes, I get the picture! You want good legs.
Jamie	Fat chance of that, though, so money will have to do.
Peter	Well, we haven't got any money, but I can give you something else: in the name of Jesus, stand up.
Narrator	Before Jamie could ask what was going on, he felt his toes tingling. Then the tingling spread, until the whole of each leg was burning. And what do you do if you burn your foot? You jump around a bit! So that's what Jamie did!
Jamie	Wow! What happened?
John	God made your legs better.
Jamie	Well, we'd better go and thank him!
Narrator	Jamie dragged Peter and John into the temple. Everyone was amazed to see him there.
John	That happened because we acted like Jesus.
Peter	You mean, by healing his legs?
John	No, by listening to what he *really* wanted. Just think, if we'd had any money, he might still be sitting there!

God Has No Favourites

Based on Acts 10

Narrator	Cornelius was a Roman officer. He had a lot of Jewish friends, but he was sad that they weren't allowed to visit him. One day, an angel came to see him
Angel	God's sent me to say how pleased he is with you.
Cornelius	Well, bless me!
Angel	Give me time, I was just coming to that. You're to send for a man called Simon Peter, who's staying at Joppa. He's lodging near the sea front with a leather worker called Simon.
Cornelius	*(Calls out)* Antonio, I've got a job for you.
Antonio	Oh, dear, Sir! You haven't got blood on your best tunic again, have you? I do wish you'd be more careful. It's off-the-peg battledress for killing and mutilating, and made to measure tunic and kilt for parades only.
Cornelius	No, don't worry, Antonio – it's not that. I want you to go and look for a leatherworker.
Antonio	Obviously a case of 'hide and seek'. Get it? You see sir, 'hide' is another name for – oh, never mind.
Cornelius	Quite. He's in Joppa. He lives right by the sea front.
Antonio	I suppose when he goes home he goes 'back to front'! A pun, you see, sir – when he – Oh what's the use!
Cornelius	I want you to ask for a man called Peter.
Antonio	That sounds Okay. I'll just knock an the door and say –
Cornelius	I think the sooner you leave the better, don't you?
Antonio	*(Aside)* Not much to ask, is it? Just to work for a master with a sense of humour, who knows his ceremonial uniform from his battle fatigues – that's all!

Narrator	Antonio did as he was told.

- He *pulled on his boots*
- and he *buttoned up his coat*
- and he *rode off on his horse*

	Meanwhile, Peter was on the flat roof of Simon's house praying. He was hungry, and had an amazing vision. He saw a great sailcloth coming out of the sky, and in it were lots and lots of different animals. Then God spoke to him.
God	There you are, Peter. Eat one of those.
Peter	You know I can only eat ritually clean food!
God	If I say something's clean, who are you to disagree?
Narrator	This happened three times, and while Peter was wondering what it meant, he heard a voice at the door.
Antonio	Hello, I've come to see Peter. Can I see him, or is Peter out? Tee hee hee! Get it? Oh, please yourself!
Peter	Oh, no! Not an amateur comedian. Tell him he can't come in – he's a foreigner and he's not ritually pure.
Antonio	I heard that. It was your God who told my boss to send for you so don't come that purity malarkey with me.
Narrator	Then Peter remembered what God had said.
God	If I say something's clean, who are you to disagree?'
Narrator	Peter went to see Cornelius. Cornelius was baptised, and became a follower of Jesus, and Antonio did too.
Peter	I've learnt a lot today. God really does love everyone, and he has no favourites.
Cornelius	Does that mean he'll fix things so that I don't have to put up with Antonio telling me those dreadful jokes?
Peter	No, I'm afraid not.